THIS BOOK BELONGS TO:

A boy's BOOK

PaRragon

Bath · New York · Singapore · Hong Kong · Cologne · Delhi · Melbourne

This is a Parragon Publishing Book
This edition published in 2007

Parragon Publishing
Queen Street House
4 Queen Street
Bath BA1 1HE, UK

Designers: Timothy Shaner and Christopher Measom
Project Director: Alice Wong
Project Assistants: Jacinta O'Halloran, Lawrence Chesler, and Nicholas Liu
Activities and Recipes by Monique Peterson
Heroines text by David Cashion
Introductions to literary excerpts by Sara Baysinger
Additional text by Sara Baysinger, Rachel Hertz, and Deidra Garcia
Production Assistants: Kate Shaw and Naomi Irie
Activities line illustrations by Lawrence Chesler

Printed in Thailand.

Contents

A boy is Truth with dirt on its face,

Beauty with a cut on its finger,

Wisdom with bubble gum on its hair,

And Hope of the future with a
frog in its pocket.

—Alan Marsh

Before it was a book, Peter Pan played to packed crowds in the London theater production called *Peter and Wendy* (1904). With the exception of a short interval during World War II, the play has run every Christmas since. The novel also first appeared under the title *Peter and Wendy*, but was not published until 1911. So how did Scottish writer Sir James Matthew Barrie (1860-1937) dream up the boy who refuses to grow up? Like Lewis Carroll, author of *Alice's Adventures in Wonderland*, Barrie had a real-life model for his main character in the form of young Peter Davies. Barrie "adopted" the five Davies boys as his companions, and would often make use of their observations and make-believe adventures in his stories. Peter Pan, too, wishes for some companions. So when he enters the nursery in search of his lost shadow, he convinces the Darling children to fly with him to Neverland, where they have many adventures together. The wicked Captain Hook means to spoil their fun, however. Will Peter finally defeat his archenemy and rescue Wendy Darling?

"Fling the girl overboard," cried Hook; and they made a rush at the figure in the cloak.

"There's none can save you now, missy," Mullins hissed jeeringly.

"There's one," replied the figure.

"Who's that?"

"Peter Pan the avenger!" came the terrible answer; and as he spoke Peter flung off his cloak. Then they all knew who 'twas that had been undoing them in the cabin, and twice Hook essayed to speak and twice he failed.
In that frightful moment I think his fierce heart broke.

At last he cried, "Cleave him to the brisket," but without conviction.

"Down, boys, and at them," Peter's voice rang out; and in another moment the clash of arms was resounding through the ship. Had the pirates kept together it is certain that they would have won; but the onset came when they were all unstrung, and they ran hither and thither, striking wildly, each thinking himself the last survivor of the crew. Man to man they were the stronger; but they fought on the defensive only, which enabled the boys to hunt in pairs and choose their quarry. Some of the miscreants leaped into the sea; others hid in dark recesses, where they were found by Slightly, who did not fight, but ran about

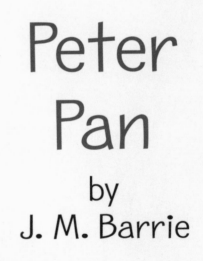

Peter
Pan
by
J. M. Barrie

with a lantern which he flashed in their faces, so that they were half blinded and fell an easy prey to the reeking swords of the other boys. There was little sound to be heard but the clang of weapons, an occasional screech or splash, and Slightly monotonously counting—five—six—seven—eight—nine—ten—eleven.

I think all were gone when a group of savage boys surrounded Hook, who seemed to have a charmed life, as he kept them at bay in that circle of fire. They had done for his dogs, but this man alone seemed to be a match for them all. Again and again they closed upon him, and again and again he hewed a clear space. He had lifted up one boy with his hook, and was using him as a buckler, when another, who had just passed his sword through Mullins, sprang into the fray.

"Put up your swords, boys," cried the newcomer, "this man is mine."

"Proud and insolent youth," said Hook, "prepare to meet thy doom."

Thus suddenly Hook found himself face to face with Peter. The others drew back and formed a ring round them.

For long the two enemies looked at one another; Hook shuddering slightly, and Peter with the strange smile upon his face.

"So, Pan," said Hook at last, "this is all your doing."

"Ay, James Hook," came the stern answer, "it is all my doing."

"Proud and insolent youth," said Hook, "prepare to meet thy doom."

"Dark and sinister man," Peter answered, "have at thee."

Without more words they fell to and for a space there was no advantage to either blade. Peter was a superb swordsman, and parried with dazzling rapidity; ever and anon he followed up a feint with a lunge that got past his foe's defense, but his shorter reach stood him in ill stead, and he could not drive the steel home. Hook, scarcely his inferior in brilliancy, but not quite so nimble in wrist play, forced him back by the weight of his onset, hoping suddenly to end all with a favorite thrust, taught him long ago by Barbecue at Rio; but to his astonishment he found this thrust turned aside again and again. Then he sought to close and give the quietus with his iron hook, which all this time had been pawing the air; but Peter doubled under it and, lunging fiercely, pierced him in the ribs. At sight of his own blood, whose peculiar color, you remember, was offensive to him, the sword fell from Hook's hand, and he was at Peter's mercy.

"Now!" cried all the boys, but with a magnificent gesture Peter invited his opponent to pick up his sword. Hook did so instantly, but with a tragic feeling that Peter was showing good form.

Hitherto he had thought it was some fiend fighting him, but darker suspicions assailed him now.

"Pan, who and what art thou?" he cried huskily.

"I'm youth, I'm joy," Peter answered at a venture, "I'm a little bird that has broken out of the egg."

This, of course, was nonsense; but it was

Seeing Peter slowly advancing upon him through the air with dagger poised, he sprang upon the bulwarks to cast himself into the sea.

14

proof to the unhappy Hook that Peter did not know in the least who or what he was, which is the very pinnacle of good form.

"To 't again," he cried despairingly.

He fought now like a human flail, and every sweep of that terrible sword would have severed in twain any man or boy who obstructed it; but Peter fluttered round him as if the very wind it made blew him out of the danger zone. And again and again he darted in and pricked.

Hook was fighting now without hope. That passionate breast no longer asked for life; but for one boon it craved: to see Peter show bad form before it was cold forever.

Abandoning the fight he rushed into the powder magazine and fired it.

"In two minutes," he cried, "the ship will be blown to pieces."

Now, now, he thought, true form will show.

But Peter issued from the powder magazine with the shell in his hands, and calmly flung it overboard.

"Pan, who and what art thou?" he cried huskily. "I'm youth, I'm joy," Peter answered. . . .

What sort of form was Hook himself showing? Misguided man though he was, we may be glad, without sympathizing with him, that in the end he was true to the traditions of his race. The other boys were flying around him now, flouting, scornful; and as he staggered about the deck striking up at them impotently, his mind was no longer with them; it was slouching in the playing fields of long ago, or being sent up for good, or watching the wallgame from a famous wall. And his shoes were right, and his waistcoat was right, and his tie was right, and his socks were right.

James Hook, thou not wholly unheroic figure, farewell.

For we have come to his last moment.

Seeing Peter slowly advancing upon him through the air with dagger poised, he sprang upon the bulwarks to cast himself into the sea. He did not know that the crocodile was waiting for him; for we purposely stopped the clock that this knowledge might be spared him: a little mark of respect from us at the end.

He had one last triumph, which I think we need not grudge him. As he stood on the bulwark looking over his shoulder at Peter gliding through the air, he invited him with a gesture to use his foot. It made Peter kick instead of stab.

At last Hook had got the boon for which he craved.

"Bad form," he cried jeeringly, and went content to the crocodile.

Thus perished James Hook.

Blast Off!

Test the boundaries of speed and aerodynamics in your own backyard with rockets and race cars. Imagine that you're a NASA engineer and launch your own spaceship into orbit. Or perhaps you're a NASCAR racer testing how far your go-cart can travel on your own hot air. Get some friends together (and grown-ups, too) and see who'll break the next speed record!

Film Canister Rocket

Toilet paper tube, paper plate, tape, colored markers, construction paper, scissors, film canister, Alka-Seltzer tablet, water

NOTE: *This activity should be done outdoors with adult supervision.*

1. To make your rocket launcher, place one end of the toilet paper tube in the center of the paper plate. Tape it in place. Decorate your launcher with colored markers.
2. For the body of your rocket, cut a strip of construction paper about 5 x 4 inches. Wrap it around the film canister lengthwise, just underneath the lid. Tape it in place.
3. To make the top of your rocket, cut a circle out of construction paper about 4 inches in diameter. Make a single cut from the outside edge to the center of the circle.

Twist the circle into a cone shape and tape. Tape your cone to the top of the rocket body (the end opposite the film canister lid.)

4. Remove the lid to the film canister and drop in the Alka-Seltzer tablet and some water. Quickly reseal the film canister and position your rocket, lid down, in the launcher. The cone should be pointing toward the sky.

5. Stand back and prepare for launch!

Balloon Go-Cart Races

Clean Styrofoam meat or produce tray, scissors, four Styrofoam coffee cups, compass, four straight pins, flexi-straw, balloon, tape, ruler

1. For the base of your go-cart, trim the edges of the Styrofoam tray so that you have a flat base.

2. Cut the bases off the Styrofoam cups to use as wheels. Use your compass to find the center of each wheel, and mark it.

Attach the wheels to the base of your go-cart by pushing a straight pin into the center of each circle and then into the Styrofoam tray. These pins will serve as axles for your wheels, so be careful not to push them in too tightly.

3. Place the sipping end of the flexi-straw into the balloon opening. Tape it in place so that you can blow up the balloon through the other end of the straw. (First, you may want to blow the balloon up a few times to stretch the rubber. This will make it easier to blow up the balloon through the straw.)

4. Tape the middle of the straw lengthwise along the center of your go-cart.

5. Mark a starting point on a smooth surface for your racetrack. Gentlemen, on your marks . . .

6. Get set . . . Blow the balloon up through the straw. Pinch the straw end to prevent the air from releasing.

7. GO! Release the straw end and see how far your go-cart goes!

Tip: For best results, do this with a few friends.

Nothing starts the day quite like a hot dish of eggs and hash browns. Frittatas are baked omelettes with just about anything in them that you like. In addition to the regular "suspects," try tossing in leftover spaghetti or fried rice! Next time you have tacos for dinner, save the leftovers for breakfast burritos! You can't get waffles as scrumptious as these variations. Make them on the weekend and freeze to toast later in the week for a quick and easy breakfast!

CRISPY WAFFLES

2 cups flour
1 tablespoon baking powder
2 cups milk
1/3 cup vegetable oil
2 eggs, separated

1. Preheat a waffle iron.
2. In a large bowl, mix flour and baking powder.
3. Add milk, oil, and egg yolks. Beat together with hand mixer until smooth.
4. In a separate bowl, whip egg whites until stiff. Gently fold into waffle batter.
5. Spoon about 1/3 cup batter onto waffle grids. Close waffle iron and bake until golden and crisp, about 2 to 3 minutes.

TRY THESE VARIATIONS:

BANANA NUT

Mash one banana and fold into batter. Chop 1/2 cup pecans or walnuts and set aside. Pour batter onto waffle grid and then sprinkle a few teaspoons of nuts on top. Bake as directed.

BACON AND CHEESE

Fry 8 strips of bacon and crumble. Set aside. Grate 1/2 cup cheddar cheese and fold into batter. Pour batter onto waffle grid and sprinkle crumbled bacon on top. Bake as directed.

CHOCOLATE PEANUT BUTTER

Fold 1 cup of chocolate chips into waffle batter and bake as directed. Spread peanut butter and honey on top of waffles and serve warm.

BREAKFAST BURRITOS

8 eggs
salt and pepper to taste
4 tortillas
1 tablespoon butter
$^1/_2$ cup cheddar or Monterey Jack cheese
1 avocado, diced
$^1/_4$ cup scallions, diced (optional)
4 strips bacon, fried and crumbled
8 teaspoons salsa

1. In a small bowl, beat eggs with a fork until blended. Add a dash of salt and pepper if desired. Meanwhile, heat oven to 250°F and warm tortillas on middle rack.
2. Melt butter in a skillet over medium heat.
3. Pour eggs into skillet and cook for 1 to 2 minutes. Gently stir with a spatula to let the uncooked egg settle at the bottom of the pan. Cook for another minute or until eggs are done to your liking.
4. Remove tortillas from oven and put onto plates. Divide the eggs evenly and spoon onto an outer third of each tortilla.
5. Add even amounts of cheese, avocado, scallions, bacon, and salsa on top of eggs.
6. To roll into burritos, fold in tortilla at sides, then roll tortilla edge with mixture toward other edge.

Makes 4 servings.

HEAVENLY HASH BROWNS

2 large baking potatoes
2 tablespoons butter
salt and pepper to taste

1. Scrub potatoes and grate them with the skins.
2. Melt butter in a large skillet over medium-high heat.
3. Add potatoes. Spread the potatoes evenly in the skillet and pat them down with a spatula. Sprinkle salt and pepper on top.
4. Fry potatoes until brown and crispy on the bottom, 5 to 8 minutes.
5. Flip the potatoes, in sections if necessary. Fry for another 5 minutes, or until brown and crispy. Serve hot with ketchup or salsa.

Makes 4 servings.

KITCHEN-SINK FRITTATAS

6 eggs
salt and pepper
2 cups leftovers
1 1/2 tablespoons butter

WESTERN: ham, cheese, peppers, green onions
GREEK: feta cheese, olives, plum tomatoes,
  spinach
SOUTHWEST: salsa, avocado, corn, Monterey
  Jack cheese, jalapeños, cilantro
ITALIAN: sausage, tomatoes, garlic, basil,
  Parmesan cheese
DOWN EAST: smoked salmon, dill, cream cheese
VEGGIE: zucchini, tomatoes, mozzarella cheese,
  broccoli, mushrooms

1. Preheat oven broiler.
2. Whisk eggs in a large bowl. Season with salt and pepper to taste.
3. Mix in all other ingredients except butter.
4. In a large ovenproof skillet, melt butter over medium heat.
5. Add egg mixture and cook until the bottom and edges are set, but eggs are still runny on top.
6. Remove skillet from stovetop and place under broiler. Broil about 3 minutes, until eggs are set and top is slightly browned.
7. Let frittata cool for a few minutes, then cut into wedges, and serve.

Makes 4 servings.

A Walk in the Woods

Learn how to discover true north without a compass, and how to figure out your average land speed. Knowing the pace at which you walk can help you estimate the time it will take you to complete a hike of known distance. As the Boy Scouts say, "Be prepared!"

FINDING TRUE NORTH

Stick, rope, two small pebbles

1. About 11 A.M., before the sun hits its highest point, push your stick straight into the ground.
2. Using the stick's shadow for the radius length, form a circle around your stick with the rope.
3. Place a pebble where the tip of the stick's shadow touches the edge of your circle.
4. Now wait. At about 1 P.M., the tip of the stick's shadow will touch the edge of the circle at another spot. Place your second pebble on that spot.
5. The imaginary straight line that connects the two pebbles is a true indication of an east-west line. The first pebble is the west end of the line. If you put your left foot on the first pebble, and your right foot on the second, you will be facing true north!

DEAD RECKONING

Tape measure, stopwatch, calculator

1. With a tape measure, mark two points on the ground 100 feet apart.
2. Use a stopwatch to count the number of seconds it takes you to walk from one marker to the next.
3. Walk the 100 feet a total of four times and find your average time by adding all the times together and dividing by four.
4. Then divide your average by 100. This will be your time (in seconds) per foot.
5. If you multiply that number by 60, you will have your average distance (in feet) per minute.
6. When you are walking, multiply your distance/minute ratio by the number of minutes you've been out. Then, if you divide that number by 5,280 (the number of feet in a mile), you'll know approximately how many miles you've gone.

NEIL ARMSTRONG (b. 1930) flew over two hundred different kinds of aircraft for the U.S. Navy in the 1950s before becoming the first man to walk on the moon. In July 1969, he was the commander of the Apollo 11 spacecraft, part of the first lunar landing mission. People all over the world watched Armstrong on their television sets as he put the first footprint on the moon and said, "That's one small step for a man, one giant leap for mankind."

DANIEL BOONE (1734–1820) grew up in the early days of America in the wilds of Pennsylvania and North Carolina. This great frontiersmen spent his childhood hunting, roaming the woods, and befriending Native Americans. He grew up to be a legendary trailblazer who helped create the Wilderness Road, which ran from eastern Virginia into Kentucky and beyond, and became the main route to the region then known as the West.

JACQUES COUSTEAU (1910–97) helped invent the Aqua-Lung, or SCUBA (self-contained underwater-breathing apparatus),

HEROES OF ADVENTURE & EXPLORATION

viewers discovered the sea world of sharks, fish, coral reefs, and sunken treasure for the first time. Over his lifetime, Cousteau traveled more than 1 million miles and made more than eighty expeditions worldwide.

LEWIS & CLARK are probably the most famous discovery team in American history. After serving as private secretary to Thomas Jefferson, Meriwether Lewis (1774–1809) was asked by the president to lead an exploration trek from St. Louis across uncharted land all the way to the Pacific Ocean. Remembering William Clark (1770–1838), a fellow soldier with a lot of frontier experience, Lewis asked his friend to help him head up the Corps of Discovery expedition. They left in 1804 and returned in 1806, and their trip together was responsible for further exploration and settlement of a vast territory.

CHARLES A. LINDBERGH (1902–74) grew up on a farm in Minnesota but had a great talent for all things mechanical, so his mother and U.S. congressman father encouraged him to pursue his abilities. Eventually, he went to college and studied engineering and then went on to flight school. All that hard work and studying paid off when in 1927 he became the first person to fly solo across the Atlantic Ocean. He piloted his plane, the *Spirit of St. Louis*, the 3600 miles from New York to Paris in 33 1/2 hours.

U R S

The "terrible lizards" once reigned over the Earth, but today we have only their bones as evidence that they existed. They ranged in all different shapes and sizes, from the behemoth brachiosaurus to the chicken-like compsognathus. Some had teeth the size of saws, and others may even have had feathers! Whatever else their fossils tell us, though, one thing is certain: It was a time when reptiles were king.

APATOSAURUS (a.k.a. *Brontosaurus*) Apatosaurus was a gentle giant. Measuring up to 90 feet long and weighing 70,000 pounds, with a tiny brain and a whip-like tail, apatosaurus left footprints a yard wide. He had to have grazed constantly to fill his enormous body. Apatosaurus lived during the late Jurassic period.

DINOSAURS

ARCHAEOPTERYX

Archaeopteryx was the world's earliest known bird. Not much bigger than a grown-up's hand, archaeopteryx lived in the late Jurassic period and was related to the dinosaurs—in fact, archaeopteryx was a lot like a reptile, only it had feathers!

BRACHIOSAURUS

At 120,000 pounds, Brachiosaurus was the heaviest creature that ever walked the earth. Brachiosaurus got its name, meaning "arm lizard," from its unusually long forelegs. Its head towered 50 feet above the ground and each of its neck vertebrae was 3 feet long! Brachiosaurus was a plant eater and lived during the late Jurassic period.

COMPSOGNATHUS

Compsognathus was the smallest dinosaur. At 3 feet long and about 6.5 pounds, he was only a little bit bigger than a chicken. This meat eater, whose name means "pretty jaw," walked on his hind legs and had two claws on each of his forelegs. Compsognathus lived during the late Jurassic period in what is now western Europe.

When Dinosaurs Lived

All the dinosaurs lived during the Mesozoic Era, which lasted from 248 million years ago until the great extinction, which happened 65 million years ago. The Mesozoic is divided into three periods:

The TRIASSIC (245 to 208 million years ago), when most of the dinosaurs' smaller ancestors lived on one great land mass.

The JURASSIC (208 to 144 million years ago), when dinosaurs developed and grew enormous, and the land split into two continents.

The CRETACEOUS (144 to 65 million years ago), when the continents split up further, and dinosaur species became separated.

DINOSAURS

PTERODACTYL
(*Pterosaur*)

Meaning "wing finger," pterodactylus (one of the smallest of the pterosaurs) was a flying reptile who lived during the Cretaceous period. With hollow bones and leathery wings that spanned three feet, pterodactylus was a small but fierce dinosaur. His ability to fly made him a terror to creatures of the sea, which were his favorite lunch.

TRICERATOPS
Triceratops is named for the three horns on his face—horns that could be up to 3 feet long, coming out of a face and neck frill that could be 7 feet wide! These plant eaters from the late Cretaceous period were a tough bunch—many skeletons show wounds from fights.

STEGOSAURUS
Though stegosaurus could be 30 feet long and weigh nearly 7,000 pounds, his brain was only the size of a walnut! He was a gentle herbivore from the late Jurassic period whose plates sticking up from his spine made him stand out from the crowd. He defended himself with the 4-foot-long spikes at the end of his tail.

DINOSAURS

TYRANNOSAURUS REX

Everyone's favorite monster, Tyrannosaurus rex's name means "king of the tyrant reptiles." Rex lived during the late Cretaceous period and was the biggest carnivorous dinosaur to live in any era. He was about 15 feet tall and 40 feet long, and weighed 12,000 pounds. His teeth, 6 inches long and serrated, were not to be argued with!

ULTRASAURUS (*Supersaurus*)

Ultrasaurus is a mystery dinosaur—only the bones of one leg have been found. But if scientists are correct about the leg's clues, ultrasaurus could be the biggest land animal ever (its leg bones are a third larger than brachiosaurus's)! Ultrasaurus roamed what is now North America in the early Cretaceous period.

VELOCIRAPTOR

The velociraptor, whose name means "speedy predator," was about 6 feet from teeth to tail. One nearly complete velociraptor skeleton has survived all those years since the Cretaceous period—and it was found curled in an attack position, holding tight to the skeleton of another dinosaur. A true fight to the death!

Peekaboo Periscope

You're a naval commander navigating uncharted seas. You're a spelunker exploring new cave passageways. You're a secret agent with special gadgets that let you peer around corners without being seen. All you need is a periscope, and you can be all of the above. Ask your mom, aunt, or big sister for some old cosmetic-case mirrors—and get ready to start looking at things from a new perspective!

Scissors, cardboard tubes (from wrapping paper, paper towels, or toilet paper), small mirrors, Scotch tape, black electrician's tape (optional)

1. Trim one end of a short cardboard tube at about a 45-degree angle. Do the same for a long tube. Make sure that the two trimmed tubes fit together perpendicularly so that they form a right angle.
2. Tape one edge of a mirror inside the trimmed opening of the long tube. Position the mirror at the joint between the long and short tubes so that it rests at a 45-degree angle opposite to the direction of the joint. Tape the other edge of the mirror inside the short tube. Tape the outsides of the tubes together so they form a 90-degree angle.
3. Repeat the same process for the opposite end of the long tube. You can face the short tubes in opposite directions, or you can build a U if you want to see what's behind you! Tape the second mirror in place so that it is parallel to the first.
4. Look in one end of your periscope, and you'll be able to see whatever the other end is facing. You can give your periscope a sleek look by wrapping it in electrician's tape.

'Whoso pulleth out this sword is by right of birth King of England.' So reads the inscription on the sword in the stone. In the legend of King Arthur, the people of England take these words seriously, as there is no heir to the throne. What follows is the story that begins a new life for young Arthur, nicknamed "the Wart" in his youth, who is the adopted son of Sir Ector and foster-brother of Kay.

Young Arthur, who struggles both to become a man and to be considered an equal to his older brother Kay, finds a wonderful mentor in the magician Merlin. The wise magician instructs young Arthur in unorthodox and imaginative ways, ultimately teaching Arthur that experience is the very best learning tool in life.

Long, long ago, after Uther Pendragon died, there was no king in Britain, and every knight hoped to seize the crown for himself. The country was like to fare ill when laws were broken on every side, and the corn which was to give the poor bread was trodden underfoot, and there was none to bring the evildoer to justice. Then, when things were at their worst, came forth Merlin the magician, and fast he rode to the place where the Archbishop of Canterbury had his dwelling. And they took counsel together, and agreed that all the lords and gentlemen of Britain should ride to London and meet on Christmas Day, now at hand, in the Great Church. So this was done. And on Christmas morning, as they left the church, they saw in the churchyard a large stone, and on it a bar of steel, and in the steel a naked sword was held, and about it was written in letters of gold, "Whoso pulleth out this sword is by right of birth King of England." They marveled at these words, and called for the archbishop, and brought him into the place where the stone stood. Then those knights who fain would be king could not hold themselves back, and they tugged at the sword with all their might; but it never stirred. The archbishop watched

The Drawing of the Sword

them in silence, but when they were faint from pulling he spoke: "The man is not here who shall lift out that sword, nor do I know were to find him. But this is my counsel—that two knights be chosen, good and true men, to keep guard over the sword."

Thus it was done. But the lords and the gentlemen-at-arms cried out that every man had a right to try to win the sword, and they decided that on New Year's Day a tournament should be held, and any knight who would, might enter the lists.

So on New Year's Day, the knights, as their custom was, went to hear service in the Great Church, and after it was over they met in the field to make ready for the tourney. Among them was a brave knight called Sir Ector, who brought with him Sir Kay, his son, and Arthur, Key's foster-brother. Now Kay had unbuckled his sword the evening before, and in his haste to be at the tourney had forgotten to put it on again and he begged Arthur to ride back and fetch it for him. But when Arthur reached the house the door was locked, for the women ha gone out to see the tourney, and though Arthur tried his best to get in he could not. Then he rode away in great anger, and said to himself, "Kay shall not be without a sword this day. I will take that sword in the churchyard and give it to him"; and he galloped fast till he reached the gate of the churchyard. Here he jumped down and tied his horse tightly to a tree, then, running up to the stone, he seized the handle of the sword, and easily drew it out; afterwards he mounted his horse again and delivered the sword to Sir Kay.

> "The man is not here who shall lift out that sword, nor do I know were to find him."

38

The moment Sir Kay saw the sword he knew it was not his own, but the sword of the stone, and he sought out his father, Sir Ector, and said to him, "Sir, this is the sword of the stone, therefore I am the rightful king." Sir Ector made no answer, but signed to Kay and Arthur to follow him, and they all three went back to the church. Leaving their horses outside, they entered the choir, and here Sir Ector took a holy book and bade Sir Kay swear how he came by that sword. "My brother Arthur gave it to me," replied Sir Kay. "How did you come by it?" asked Sir Ector, turning to Arthur, "Sir," said Arthur, "when I rode home for my brother's sword I found no one to deliver it to me, and as I resolved he should not be swordless I thought of the sword in this stone, and I pulled it out." "Were any knights present when you did this?" asked Sir Ector. "No, none," said Arthur. "Then it is you," said Sir Ecotr, "who are the rightful king of this land." "But why am I the king?" enquired Arthur. "Because," answered Sir Ector, "this is an enchanted sword, and no man could draw it but he who was born a king. Therefore put the sword back into the stone, and let me see you take it out." "That is soon done," said Arthur replacing the sword, and Sir Ector himself tried to draw it, but he could not. "Now it is your turn," he said to Sir Kay, but Sir Kay

"...when I rode home for my brother's sword I found no one to deliver it to me, and as I resolved he should not be swordless I thought of the sword in this stone, and I pulled it out."

fared no better than his father, though he tugged with all his might and main. "Now you, Arthur," and Arthur pulled it out as easily as if it had been lying in its sheath, and as he did so Sir Ector and Sir Kay sank to their knees before him. "Why do you, my father and brother, kneel to me?" asked Arthur in surprise. "Nay, nay, my lord," answered Sir Ector, "I was never your father, though till today I did not know who your father really was. You are the son of Uther Pendragon, and you were brought to me when you were born by Merlin himself, who promised that when the time came I should know from whom you sprang. And now it has been revealed to me." But when Arthur heard that Sir Ector was not his father, he wept bitterly. "If I am king," he said at last, "ask what you will, and I shall not fail you. For to you, and to my lady and mother, I owe more than to anyone in the world, for she loved me and treated me as her son."

And on the Twelfth Day the knights and barons came again, but none could draw it out but Arthur.

"Sir," replied Sir Ector, "I only ask that you will make your foster-brother, Sir Kay, seneschal* of all your lands."

"That I will readily," answered Arthur, "and while he and I live no other shall fill that office."

Sir Ector then bade them seek out the archbishop with him, and they told him all that had happened concerning the sword, with Arthur had left standing in the stone. And on the Twelfth Day the knights and barons came again, but none could draw it out but Arthur. When they saw this, many of the barons became angry and cried out that they would never own a boy for king whose blood was not

41

better than their own. So it was agreed to wait till Candlemas, when more knights might be there, and meanwhile the same two men who had been chosen before watched the sword night and day; but at Candlemas it was the same thing, and at Easter. And when Pentecost came, the common people who were present, and saw Arthur pull out the sword, cried with one voice that he was their king, and they would kill any man who said differently. Then rich and poor fell on their knees before him, and Arthur took the sword and offered it upon the altar where the archbishop stood, and the best man that was there made him knight. After that the crown was put on his head, and he swore to his lords and commons that he would be a true king, and would do them justice all the days of his life.

* "Seneschal" means steward.

Arthur took the sword and offered it upon the altar where the archbishop stood, and the best man that was there made him knight.

FRISBEE GOLF

Aim and Toss

Number of players: two or more

What you need: a Frisbee, a large open area, paper and pencil for keeping score

Before play begins, everyone decides on what the "hole" will be—it can be a particular tree in the field, a pole, or whatever else serves as a large target. To make things interesting, the players also might decide on what "hazards" and obstacles to put on the way to the hole, like having to throw through an empty jungle gym, or a tunnel perhaps. Each player then takes a turn throwing the Frisbee as many times as it takes to reach the target. The fewer number of throws, the better. You can design numerous "holes" like these for an entire course.

TENNIS BALL ULTIMATE

Passing the Ball

Number of players: six or more

What you need: a tennis ball, a large open area

One team starts off as offense, while the other is defense. The goal of the game is to get the ball across your team's scoring line at one end of the field, but only by passing. Whoever has the ball is not allowed to move from his position until he passes it. Meanwhile, defending players can try to block or catch the throw, but they are not allowed to actually touch the thrower. If the thrower is unable to toss the ball after 10 seconds, or if the ball hits the ground or is intercepted, it goes to the other side.

TAG

You're it!

Number of players: unlimited

What you need: exuberance

REGULAR One of the players is "it," and he chases the others around, trying to tag them. Whoever gets tagged becomes the new "it."

BALL Same as regular tag, but instead of touching other players, "it" tosses a soft rubber ball to tag others.

BLOB Only one player starts off as "it," but as he tags other players, they join hands with "it," eventually making one massive "it" blob.

FREEZE Whoever gets tagged becomes "frozen," and has to stand perfectly still until he is touched by an unfrozen player.

POISON After someone is chosen as "it," the other players place their hands on their chests and start running. If a player gets tagged, he has to place a hand where he got touched, and now he's an "it" too. By the end of the game, you will have players running around with their hands touching their arms, legs, and backs. Whoever is tagged last becomes "it" for the next round.

EGG TOSS

Catch—please!

Number of players: four or more, in even numbers

What you need: a raw egg for every two players

Players pair off. Partners stand facing each other about 3 feet apart. Players on one side each hold an egg. The object of the game is to toss your egg to your partner, and hopefully, he or she will catch it. Players who drop their egg are out of the game. Players who catch their egg must take a big step back and toss the egg again. The last set of partners left in the game are the clean champions! (For a less messy though wetter version, you can use water balloons.)

Written more than a century ago, *The Jungle Book* (1894) is the story

of Mowgli, the man-cub, who is raised by a pack of wolves, and who

befriends memorable animals of the wild: Baloo, the wise and warm

brown bear, Bagheera, the silky black panther; Kaa, the cunning and

majestic python; and the nattering monkeys. These distinctly

personified creatures nurture young Mowgli and instruct him on the

laws of the jungle. Shere Khan, the sinister tiger, eventually threatens

Mowgli's idyllic existence. A highly respected author throughout his

lifetime, Kipling (1865-1936) nevertheless refused a number of honors,

including a knighthood and the Poet Laureateship. However, he did not

dare decline the highest tribute offered him: the Nobel Prize for Literature.

In 1907, he was the first English author to receive the award.

"**S**omething is coming up hill," said Mother Wolf, twitching one ear. "Get ready."

The bushes rustled a little in the thicket, and Father Wolf dropped with his haunches under him, ready for his leap. Then, if you had been watching, you would have seen the most wonderful thing in the world—the wolf checked in mid-spring. He made his bound before he saw what it was he was jumping at, and then he tried to stop himself. The result was that he shot up straight into the air for four or five feet, landing almost where he left ground.

"Man!" he snapped. "A man's cub. Look!"

Directly in front of him, holding on by a low branch, stood a naked brown baby who could just walk—as soft and as dimpled a little atom as ever came to a wolf's cave at night. He looked up into Father Wolf's face, and laughed.

"Is that a man's cub?" said Mother Wolf. "I have never seen one. Bring it here."

A wolf accustomed to moving his own cubs can, if necessary, mouth an egg without breaking it, and though Father Wolf's jaws closed right on the child's back, not a tooth even scratched the skin, as he laid it down among the cubs.

"How little! How naked, and—how bold!" said Mother Wolf, softly. The baby was pushing his way between the cubs to get close to the warm hide. "*Ahai!* He is

The Jungle Book

by Rudyard Kipling

taking his meal with the others. And so this is a man's cub. Now, was there ever a wolf that could boast of a man's cub among her children?"

"I have heard now and again of such a thing, but never in our pack or in my time," said Father Wolf. "He is altogether without hair, and I could kill him with a touch of my foot. But see, he looks up and is not afraid."

The moonlight was blocked out of the mouth of the cave, for Shere Khan's great square head and shoulders were thrust into the entrance. Tabaqui, behind him, was squeaking: "My lord, my lord, it went in here!"

"Shere Khan does us great honor," said Father Wolf, but his eyes were very angry. "What does Shere Khan need?"

"My quarry. A man's cub went this way," said Shere Khan. "Its parents have run off. Give it to me."

Shere Khan had jumped at a woodcutters' campfire, as Father Wolf had said, and was furious from the pain of his burned feet. But Father Wolf knew that the mouth of the cave was too narrow for a tiger to come in by. Even where he was, Shere Khan's shoulders and fore paws were cramped for want of room, as a man's would be if he tried to fight in a barrel.

"The wolves are a free people," said Father Wolf. "They take orders from the head of the pack, and not from any striped cattle-

"He is altogether without hair, and I could kill him with a touch of my foot. But see, he looks up and is not afraid."

killer. The man's cub is ours—to kill if we choose."

"Ye choose and ye do not choose! What talk is this of choosing? By the bull that I killed, am I to stand nosing into your dog's den for my fair dues? It is I, Shere Khan, who speak!"

The tiger's roar filled the cave with thunder. Mother Wolf shook herself clear of the cubs and sprang forward, her eyes, like two green moons in the darkness, facing the blazing eyes of Shere Khan.

"And it is I, Raksha (the Demon), who answer. The man's cub is mine, Lungri— mine to me! He shall not be killed. He shall live to run with the pack and to hunt with the pack; and in the end, look you, hunter of little naked cubs—frog-eater— fish-killer—he shall hunt *thee!* Now get hence, or by the sambur that I killed (I eat no starved cattle), back thou goest to thy mother, burned beast of the jungle, lamer than ever thou camest into the world! Go!"

Father Wolf looked on amazed. He had almost forgotten the days when he won Mother Wolf in fair fight from five other wolves, when she ran in the pack and was not called the Demon for compliment's sake. Shere Khan might have faced Father Wolf, but he could not stand up against Mother Wolf, for he knew that where he was she had all the advantage of the ground, and would fight to the death. So he backed out of the cave-mouth growling and when he was clear he shouted:

"Each dog barks in his own yard! We will see what the pack will say to this fostering of man-cubs. The cub

The tiger's roar filled the cave with thunder.

is mine, and to my teeth he will come in the end, O bushtailed thieves!"

Mother Wolf threw herself down panting among the cubs, and Father Wolf said to her gravely:

"Shere Khan speaks this much truth. The cub must be shown to the pack. Wilt thou still keep him, Mother?"

"Keep him!" she gasped. "He came naked, by night, alone and very hungry; yet he was not afraid! Look, he has pushed one of my babes to one side already. And that lame butcher would have killed him and would have run off to the Wainganga while the villagers here hunted through all our lairs in revenge! Keep him? Assuredly I will keep him. Lie still, little frog. O thou Mowgli—for Mowgli the Frog I will call thee—the time will come when thou wilt hunt Shere Khan as he has hunted thee."

"The cub is mine, and to my teeth he will come in the end, O bushtailed thieves!"

A Song of Greatness

A Chippewa Indian Song
Transcribed by
Mary Austin

When I hear the old men
Telling of heroes,
Telling of great deeds
Of ancient days,
When I hear them telling,
Then I think within me
I too am one of these.

When I hear the people
Praising great ones,
Then I know that I too
Shall be esteemed,
I too when my time comes
Shall do mightily.

*T*his Big Bad Burger is so good—it's bad! It's sure to satisfy any appetite. For the best grilled-cheese sandwich ever, try this classic French variation, called a **Croque Monsieur**. The secret is a hot slice of ham in the middle of the melted cheese. Yum! Wraps make it easy to add just about anything to a sandwich, without food falling out the sides as you eat. But if you have a mess of an appetite, you must make the ultimate hero. Just a word of warning: You may need to invite the football team over to help you finish it!

BIG BAD BURGER

6 ounces ground beef
1 egg yolk
1 tablespoon cooked spinach, well drained
   and chopped
1 teaspoon grated onion
salt and freshly ground black pepper
1 tablespoon grated Swiss or cheddar cheese
mayonnaise, to taste
ketchup, to taste
1 wholewheat roll or hamburger bun
2 lettuce leaves, cleaned and chopped
2 slices ripe tomato

1. Preheat broiler.
2. In a large bowl, combine beef, egg yolk, spinach, onion, and salt and pepper and mix well.

3. Form three quarters of the meat mixture into a patty, and set the remaining mixture aside.
4. Make an indentation in the center of the patty, and fill it with the cheese. Cover the cheese with the remaining meat mixture, and form a finished patty.
5. Broil the patty for $2^1/_2$ to 3 minutes on each side for a juicy rare burger—or broil longer to your preference.
6. Spread mayonnaise and ketchup on each side of the wholewheat roll or toasted bun. Place the burger on the bottom half, top it with lettuce and tomato slices, and cover it with the other half of the bun.

Makes 1 serving.

BIG BITES

CROQUE MONSIEUR

4 slices bread
2 ounces Swiss cheese, thinly sliced
2 ounces Canadian bacon, thinly sliced
1^1/$_2$ tablespoons butter

1. Cover two slices of bread with ^{1}/$_2$ ounce of cheese. Layer 1 ounce of Canadian bacon, then top with remaining cheese. Cover with bread slices.
2. Melt butter in skillet over medium heat.
3. Fry sandwiches, pressing down gently with spatula, until browned on the bottom. Turn sandwiches over and fry until second side is browned.
4. Remove from skillet and cut diagonally to make triangle halves. Serve warm.

Makes 2 sandwiches.

IT'S A WRAP

Try these combinations on a plain or flavored tortilla. To wrap, fold the bottom of the tortilla about a fourth of the way up, then fold the left side over the middle and the right side over the left. Then finish rolling, pick it up, and sink your teeth into it!

TURKEY BLT

^{1}/$_8$ pound thinly sliced turkey
2 slices bacon, cooked
2–3 slices tomato
^{1}/$_4$ cup shredded lettuce
1 tablespoon creamy peppercorn or ranch dressing

VEGGIE SUPREME

1 tablespoon herbed cream cheese
^{1}/$_4$ avocado, sliced
^{1}/$_4$ yellow pepper, cut into strips
2–3 slices tomato
2–3 slices red onion
4–6 spinach leaves
2 tablespoons grated carrot
2 tablespoons alfalfa sprouts

BIG BITES

TUNA SALAD

2 leaves romaine lettuce
Blend: 3 ounces tuna fish, 1 diced pickle,
1 tablespoon mayonnaise, $1/2$ teaspoon
lemon juice

REUBEN

2 slices corned beef
1 slice Swiss cheese
3 tablespoons sauerkraut
1 tablespoon Thousand Island dressing

SKY-HIGH & MILE-LONG HERO

Slice a loaf of French bread and spread butter, mayonnaise, and mustard on both halves. Then add as much of the following ingredients as you like.

- Cheddar cheese
- Swiss cheese
- Monterey Jack cheese
- Fontina cheese
- Parmesan cheese
- mozzarella cheese
- salami
- bologna

- mortadella
- meatballs
- ham
- bacon
- fried eggs
- tomato slices
- avocado slices or guacamole
- green pepper strips

- pineapple slices
- onion rings
- pickle slices
- olives
- cole slaw
- shredded lettuce
- spinach leaves
- green chilies

It Couldn't Be Done

by Edgar A. Guest

Somebody said that it couldn't be done,
  But he with a chuckle replied
That "maybe it couldn't," but he would be one
  Who wouldn't say so till he'd tried.
So he buckled right in with the trace of a grin
  On his face. If he worried he hid it.
He started to sing as he tackled the thing
  That couldn't be done, and he did it.

Somebody scoffed: "Oh, you'll never do that;
　　At least no one ever has done it";
But he took off his coat and he took off his hat,
　　And the first thing we knew he'd begun it.
With a lift of his chin and a bit of a grin,
　　Without any doubting or quiddit,
He started to sing as he tackled the thing
　　That couldn't be done, and he did it.

There are thousands to tell you it cannot be done,
　　There are thousands to prophesy failure;
There are thousands to point out to you, one by one,
　　The dangers that wait to assail you.
But just buckle in with a bit of a grin,
　　Just take off your coat and go to it;
Just start to sing as you tackle the thing
　　That "cannot be done," and you'll do it.

GEORGE WASHINGTON CARVER (1864–1943) was born a slave on a Missouri plantation, and because of this, he never went to elementary school. Instead, after he finished his chores, he would go into the woods, do his own experiments, and teach himself about the natural world. Later, when he was a free man, Carver was the first African American to graduate from Iowa State University. His studies in farming led him to discover 325 uses for peanuts (including peanut butter) and over 100 uses for sweet potatoes. Carver also created better ways for farmers to work with soil and crops. These methods are still used today.

THOMAS ALVA EDISON (1847–1931) was probably the greatest and most productive inventor of his time. While Edison was growing up in Michigan, his teacher complained that he asked too many questions. Young Tom's parents supported his curiosity, and he set up his first science laboratory in their basement when he was ten. Edison went on to hold patents on over a thousand inventions, including the phonograph and the light bulb, and he even helped to create motion pictures.

ALBERT EINSTEIN (1879–1955) is generally thought of as one of the greatest scientists in the modern world. Einstein was born in Germany, but brought his knowledge of

THEORY OF RELATIVITY

OH, YEAH!

physics to America in the 1930s. His most famous contribution is the theory of relativity, which has to do with time, space, and the motion of objects. While Einstein's famous $E=mc^2$ equation about energy and atoms was used by scientists in the development of the nuclear bomb, this Nobel Prize-winner always worked for peace.

BENJAMIN FRANKLIN (1706–90) did much more than fly a kite in a storm and discover that lightning contains electricity: He was a diplomat, printer, philosopher, and writer, in addition to being an inventor and scientist. The list of his inventions includes bifocal eyeglasses, the lightning rod, the odometer, and the iron furnace stove, a.k.a. the Franklin stove. Toward the end of his life, he made one of his greatest contributions: signing the Declaration of Independence.

STEPHEN HAWKING (b. 1942) has not let a disease that confines him to a wheelchair and forces him to use a computerized voice box keep him from being a brilliant scientist. This English genius actually provided mathematical evidence to back up the famous big bang theory, which offers an explanation of how the universe began. His work on black holes and the connection between space and time also is celebrated.

ISAAC NEWTON (1642–1727) achieved gigantic breakthroughs in mathematics (inventing the mathematical field of calculus) and in ideas relating to color. However, Newton is probably most famous for observing an apple as it fell from a tree. From just sitting under a tree when its fruit fell from the branch, he discovered the force of gravity, and the world has never been the same.

Map It!

Plan a treasure hunt, bury a time capsule, or stake out a clubhouse. How are you going to tell your friends where to go? Make a map, of course! You don't have to be a cartographer to make a good sketch map. Whether you want to chart an area of town or a route in the country, you can incorporate common symbols to indicate natural or man-made structures, landmarks, or topography. Like every good mapmaker, be sure to add personal knowledge about the area, such as the barking dog in the used-car lot, the house with the yummiest homemade cookies, or the creek with the most tadpoles.

Sketchbook, pencil, compass, graph paper

1. Choose the area you'd like to include in your map. Then find a good reference point, like a tree, a hill, or a building, from which you can see a good portion of the area you want to map out.
2. Take some time to observe the land. Make notes in your sketchbook about your location and the roads, landmarks, and structures that are visible from your viewpoint. Use your compass to find north and include that in your sketch.
3. If possible, go to two or three different points of reference and make additional sketches. Then, using your graph paper, make a composite map from your various sketches. You'll be surprised how much you can learn about an area by mapping it!

Use these basic topographical symbols when creating your map:

Corn and Cultivated Land

Palm and Palmetto

Buildings — General

Schoolhouse

Pack Trail

Railroad — Any kind

Church

Cemetery

Ford (Wading Place)

Foot Bridge

Bridge

Lock (Point upstream)

Lake

Good Motor Road

Poor Motor Road

Town

Windmill

Quarry — Mine

Woods — Broad leaves

Woods — Pines, etc.

Grassland

Marsh

Mark Twain (1835-1910), born Samuel Langhorne Clemens, grew up in a poor family in Hannibal, Missouri. His father died when he was just twelve years old, and so Samuel was forced to abandon his childhood to help support his family. His first jobs included a printer's apprentice, a newspaper writer, and a pilot of a steamship on the Mississippi. This last occupation provided much of the material for his most famous books, *The Adventures of Tom Sawyer* and *The Adventures of Huckleberry Finn*. It was also the inspiration for his pen name. (His shipmates would shout "mark twain" to measure the depth of the river—twain equaling two fathoms.) Twain's use of language— particularly with regard to dialogue—uniquely captures the rich landscape and voice of the American frontier. His deep understanding of human nature infuses his stories with a realism that sets them apart. *The Story of Tom Sawyer*, which details his exploits with his band of friends, was published in 1876. Here we find merrily mischievous Tom joining forces with his law- less companion Huckleberry Finn to search for hidden treasure.

There comes a time in every rightly constructed boy's life when he has a raging desire to go somewhere and dig for hidden treasure. This desire suddenly came upon Tom one day. He sallied out to find Joe Harper, but failed of success. Next he sought Ben Rogers; he had gone fishing. Presently he stumbled upon Huck Finn the Red-handed. Huck would answer. Tom took him to a private place, and opened the matter to him confidentially. Huck was willing. Huck was always willing to take a hand in any enterprise that offered entertainment and required no capital, for he had a troublesome superabundance of that sort of time which is *not* money.

"Where'll we dig?" said Huck.

"Oh, 'most anywhere."

"Why, is it hid all around?"

"No, indeed it ain't. It's hid in mighty particular places, Huck—sometimes on islands, sometimes in rotten chests under the end of a limb of an old dead tree, just where the shadow falls at midnight; but mostly under the floor in ha'nted houses."

"Who hides it?"

"Why, robbers, of course— who'd you reckon? Sunday-school sup'rintendents?"

"I don't know. If it was mine I wouldn't hide it; I'd spend it and have a good time."

The Adventures of Tom Sawyer

by Mark Twain

"So would I; but robbers don't do that way, they always hide it and leave it there."

"Don't they come after it any more?"

"No, they think they will, but they generally forget the marks, or else they die. Anyway it lays there a long time and gets rusty; and by-and-by somebody finds an old yellow paper that tells how to find the marks—a paper that's got to be ciphered over about a week because it's mostly signs and hy'roglyphics."

"Hyro—which?"

"Hy'roglyphics—pictures and things, you know, that don't seem to mean anything."

"Have you got one of them papers, Tom?"

"No."

"Well, then, how you going to find out the marks?"

"I don't want any marks. They always bury it under a ha'nted house, or on an island, or under a dead tree that's got one limb sticking out. Well, we've tried Jackson's Island a little, and we can try it again sometime; and there's the old ha'nted house up the Still-House branch, and there's lots of dead-limb trees—dead loads of 'em."

"Is it under all of them?"

"How you talk! No!"

"Then how you going to know which one to go for?"

"Go for all of 'em."

"Why, Tom, it'll take all summer."

"They always bury it under a ha'nted house, or on an island, or under a dead tree that's got one limb sticking out."

"Well, what of that? Suppose you find a brass pot with a hundred dollars in it, all rusty and gay, or a rotten chest full of di'monds. How's that?"

Huck's eyes glowed.

"That's bully, plenty bully enough for me. Just you gimme the hundred dollars, and I don't want no di'monds."

"All right. But I bet you *I* ain't going to throw off on di'monds. Some of 'em's worth twenty dollars apiece. There ain't any, hardly, but's worth six bits or a dollar."

"No! Is that so?"

"Cert'nly—anybody'll tell you so. Hain't you ever seen one, Huck?"

"Not as I remember."

"Oh, kings have slathers of them."

"Well, I don't know no kings, Tom."

"I reckon you don't. But if you was to go to Europe you'd see a raft of 'em hopping around."

"Do they hop?"

"Hop?—your granny! No!"

"Well, what did you say they did for?"

"Shucks! I only meant you'd *see* 'em—scattered around, you know, in a kind of general way. Like that old hump-backed Richard."

"Richard! What's his other name?"

"He didn't have any other name. Kings don't have any but a given name."

"No?"

"But they don't."

So they got a crippled pick and a shovel, and set out on their three-mile tramp.

"Well, if they like it, Tom, all right; but I don't want to be a king and have only just a given name, like a nigger. But say—where you going to dig first?"

"Well, I don't know. S'pose we tackle that old dead limb tree on the hill t'other side of Still-House branch?"

"I'm agreed."

So they got a crippled pick and a shovel, and set out on their three-mile tramp. They arrived hot and panting, and threw themselves down in the shade of a neighboring elm to rest and have a smoke.

"I like this," said Tom.

"So do I."

"Say, Huck, if we find a treasure here, what you going to do with your share?"

"Well, I'll have a pie and a glass of soda every day, and I'll go to every circus that comes along. I'll bet I'll have a gay time."

"Well, ain't you going to save any of it?"

"Save it? What for?"

"Why, so as to have something to live on by-and-by."

"Oh, that ain't any use. Pap would come back to thish yer town some day and get his claws on it if I didn't hurry up, and I tell you he'd clean it out pretty quick. What you going to do with yourn, Tom?"

"I'm going to buy a new drum, and a sure-'nough sword, and a red necktie, and a bull-pup, and get married."

"Married!"

"That's it."

"Tom, you—why, you ain't in your right mind."

Virtual Vesuvius

There are 139 active volcanoes in North and Central America—that's more than anywhere else in the world. Some, like Mount St. Helens in Washington State, erupt once every few hundred years, covering hundreds of miles in volcanic ash. Others, like Kilauea in Hawaii have continuous non-explosive eruptions. The lava bubbles, coughs, and hisses every day. Even if you don't live near an active volcano, you can build one in your backyard with common household ingredients. How often it blows its top will be up to you.

This can be a very messy project, so ask an adult for permission before you get started. Then gather some friends and do this one outdoors for best results.

Large narrow-neck bottle, large aluminum baking tray, bubble-wrap, tape, self-drying clay, pebbles, twigs, tempera paints, paintbrushes, dried moss or lichen, glue, baking soda, paper cup, liquid dish soap, distilled vinegar, red food coloring

1. Stand the bottle in the middle of the tray. To begin building your volcano shape, form a cone by taping bubble wrap around the bottle. Do not cover the opening of the bottle. Make sure the smooth side of the bubble wrap faces out.
2. Cover the cone with clay all the way to the lip of the bottle. Mold the clay around the bottle opening to resemble a volcanic crater.

3. Press twigs and pebbles into the clay to represent trees and lava rocks. When the clay has dried, paint the surface with tempera. Then, once the paint is dry, attach moss and lichen to the surface with glue.
4. When you are ready for your volcano to erupt, pour two tablespoons of baking soda into the mouth of the bottle.
5. In a paper cup, mix about a tablespoon of liquid dish soap and about 4 ounces of vinegar. Add a few drops of red food coloring.
6. Pour the liquid mixture into the mouth of the bottle. Then stand back and watch your molten lava spew!

NOTE: *Once the baking soda has dried completely, you can add more vinegar solution to make the volcano erupt again.*

Build a Lean-to

Whether you're hiking as far as a mountain lake or as close as your backyard, you can up the adventure ante by making your own shelter. Lean-tos are easy to construct and a fun way to practice your wilderness survival skills. So grab a friend and get ready for the outdoors—come rain, snow, or wind!

Poles (you can use tent poles, broomsticks or whatever is easily available), rope, branches, boughs, canvas or tarp (optional)

1. Pick the site where you'd like to build your lean-to and check the wind direction. To shelter you, the back of your lean-to must face the wind.
2. Clear a level spot for your shelter. Look for a natural structure that might serve as a main support for your lean-to, such as some trees or a large boulder. If a natural support isn't available, you can make a frame by anchoring two poles in the ground.
3. Attach a crossbar pole to your main supports at about shoulder level, securing both ends with rope.
4. Gather long branches or poles and lean them against the crossbar. Be sure to angle them out

far enough so that you will be able to sit comfortably underneath the shelter. Block the ends of your lean-to with additional branches; if necessary, tie the end branches in place with rope. Fit the branches as closely together as possible to keep the wind out.

5. Collect lots of small boughs and sticks and, starting at the bottom, layer them like shingles against the lean-to. Moss, pine needles, and lichen-covered branches work well, too. This will help insulate your fort and keep you warm as well as sheltered from the wind. If you have a tarp or canvas, you can secure it on top to water-proof your lean-to.

ini Meatloaves pack a punch in your lunch! Eat as is or sandwich between two thick slabs of bread. Substitute ground turkey for beef for a lean and mean alternative. Cold sesame noodles make a great alternative to a sandwich, and PB & J Bars provide quick energy. Make lots of fruit chews and always have handy to throw into your lunch bag.

MINI MEATLOAVES

1¹/₂ pounds ground beef
1 cup soft bread crumbs
¹/₄ cup chopped onions
1 teaspoon dried Italian seasoning
¹/₄ cup ketchup
1¹/₂ cups zucchini, shredded
1 egg, slightly beaten
¹/₂ teaspoon salt
Muffin pan

1. Heat oven to 400° F.
2. In large bowl, combine all ingredients except ketchup, mixing thoroughly.
3. Spoon approximately ¹/₃ cup beef mixture into each of the 12 medium muffin cups. Press lightly. Spread ketchup generously over each one.
4. Bake for 20 minutes or until centers are no longer pink.
5. Remove meatloaves from pan. Let cool.
6. Freeze meatloaves and defrost as needed.
7. Pack in tupperware container with a whole-wheat bread roll and ketchup packets for a hearty lunch.

Makes 12 loaves.

FUN FRUIT CHEWS

3 cups juice (orange, pineapple, grape, mango, etc.)
five (7-gram) gelatin packets

1. In a small mixing bowl, stir gelatin into 1 cup of fruit juice. Set aside.
2. In a small saucepan, bring 1 cup of juice to a boil. Add gelatin-juice mix and stir. Stir in remaining cup of juice.
3. Remove from heat and pour into an 8-inch casserole dish. Refrigerate until firm.
4. Cut into fun shapes and wrap individually.
   Makes 18 to 24 chews. Chews will keep in the refrigerator for about a week.

COLD SESAME NOODLES

8 ounces soba (lo mein) noodles or other thin pasta cooked
6 tablespoons peanut butter or tahini
1/4 cup hot water
2 tablespoons sesame oil
1/4 cup soy sauce
1/2 teaspoon ground ginger
1 clove garlic, minced
2–3 tablespoons green onions or chives, minced
1/2 cup bean sprouts

1. In a small bowl, whisk peanut butter or tahini, hot water, sesame oil, soy sauce, ginger, and garlic together until they form a smooth paste.
2. In a large bowl, toss noodles with peanut-butter paste, green onions, and bean sprouts.
3. Refrigerate. Pack in a thermos for lunch and eat with chopsticks.

Makes 4 servings.

PB & J BARS

2 cups uncooked oats
1/3 cup peanut-butter
1/2 cup grape jelly

1. Preheat oven to 350°F.
2. In medium bowl, combine all ingredients and mix thoroughly.
3. Spread mixture into greased 8-inch-square pan.
4. Bake for 25 minutes. Let cool.
5. Cut into bars and wrap individually for lunches.

Makes 8 bars.

SUPER LUNCH-SACK STUFFERS

- Pickles
- Graham crackers "sand-wiched" with chocolate-marshmallow spread
- Pretzels
- Bananas
- Apples
- Grapes
- Peeled orange

- Baby carrots
- Cherry tomatoes
- Yogurt cups
- Pudding cups
- Apple sauce
- Juice boxes
- Crackers with sliced cheese and salami
- Fortune cookies

- Popcorn
- String cheese
- Hard-boiled eggs
- Fig bars
- Edamame
- Sunflower seeds
- Peanuts in their shells
- Homemade cookies or brownies

BETTER BROWN BAG TIPS:

- Put juice boxes or water bottles in freezer the night before. You'll have a cold drink for lunch and an ice pack to keep the rest of your lunch cool.
- Keep lettuce, tomatoes, and other "moist" foods wrapped separately. Build your sandwich at lunchtime and avoid soggy sammies!
- Pack travel-sized moist hand wipes for easy cleanup after you eat.

- Thermoses can be for more than just juice. You can keep last night's left-over spaghetti, chili, or soup warm for several hours. Or, keep pasta salads, potato salad, or fruit salads nice and cool.
- Save prepackaged condiments from your favorite take-out restaurants for extra bread-spreads or dipping sauces.

Radio

You're probably aware by now that when you turn on the car radio, your favorite band isn't hidden in the glove compartment giving you a private concert. But have you ever wondered how your radio in fact works?

Radio waves are actually made of invisible light. The longest waves in the electromagnetic spectrum, they contain low-energy light (ultraviolet rays from the sun are an example of high-energy light). These invisible waves are all around you on a constant basis. They are used to carry signals for all sorts of things you use every day: radios, televisions, cordless and cellular phones, garage door openers, baby monitors, and even your favorite remote-control car.

In the case of radios, the program you listen to, whether it is music or talk, originates in a sound booth. The disc jockey speaks into his microphone, which converts the sound waves into an electrical signal. This signal is again converted, this time to an audio wave plus a carrier wave. It is amplified and sent to the station's antenna. The converted signal stimulates the atoms in the antenna, and their electrons begin to give off invisible light that spreads into the sky.

Your radio has an antenna of its own that catches these waves because you are "tuned in" to the station. (Note: A tuner enables your radio to separate out and select the correct waves of your station from the thousands your antenna is receiving at any given moment.)

The signal that was converted at the station so it could travel to your radio is now converted back. Your speakers act as a reverse microphone, turning the electrical audio signal back into sound waves so you can hear your program loud and clear!

Light Bulbs

Light bulbs—we use them every day to see the world around us. But how do they work? Well, an incandescent light bulb is composed of a glass bulb filled with inert gas (usually argon), a coiled wire filament, and electrical contact wires. The filament wire is made out of tungsten. It has an extremely high melting point. When an electrical current is delivered to the filament via the electrical contact wires, the filament heats up so much that it glows. This is what we see as light.

The reduced-pressure inert gas is there to keep the metal from mixing with oxygen in the air, which would cause the tungsten wire to burn out. When a filament does burn out, it is because over time the tungsten wire vaporizes. The black dust that settles on the inside of the glass is the resolidified tungsten metal.

The problem with incandescent light bulbs is that the heat wastes a lot of electricity. Heat is not light, and energy spent creating heat in order to create light is a waste.

A florescent bulb uses a different method to produce light. An electric current is passed through mercury vapor in the florescent tube. The vapor emits ultraviolet rays that hit the phosphor coating on the inside of the tube. The phosphor emits white light. A fluorescent bulb produces less heat, so it is much more efficient. A 15-watt fluorescent bulb will produce the same amount of light as a 60-watt incandescent bulb.

Young Athletes

BASEBALL

On July 22, 1887, FREDERICK JOSEPH CHAPMAN (1872–1957) was 14 years, 239 days old when he pitched for Philadelphia in the American Association, becoming the youngest player in professional baseball history. He did not play again, however.

BASKETBALL

When JERMAINE O'NEAL (b. 1978) made his professional basketball debut with the Portland Trailblazers on December 5, 1996, he became the youngest-ever NBA player, at 18 years, 53 days of age.

EXPLORING

At the age of 10, ROBERT SCHUMANN (b. 1982), of the UK, and his father decided to go vacationing at the North Pole. Arriving there by plane on April 6, 1992, Schumann became the youngest explorer ever to arrive at the northernmost point of the planet. On December 29, 1993, at age 11, he reached the South Pole by mountain bike, having flown to within a short distance of his destination.

HIKING

MICHAEL COGSWELL was 6 years old when he finished hiking the length of the approximately 2,160-mile-long (3,476-km) Appalachian Trail with his mother and stepfather in 1980. It took them eight and a half months to finish the world's longest designated footpath, which stretches from Katahdin, Maine, to Springer Mountain, Georgia.

MOUNTAIN CLIMBING

Although his age at the time is still somewhat in dispute, Nepal's SHAMBU TAMANG (b. 1955) became the youngest person ever to ascend 29,035-foot-high (8,850-meter) Mt. Everest, on May 5, 1973. He's thought to have been 17 years, 6 months, and 15 days old when he reached the summit.

OLYMPICS

ROBERT BRUCE MATTHIAS (b. 1930) became the youngest male Olympic champion when he won the decathlon, held August 5–6 in the 1948 Olympic Games, in London. He was 17 years, 263 days old.

SOCCER

EDSON ARANTES DO NASCIMENTO (b. 1940), better known as Pelé, distinguished himself as the youngest scorer in a World Cup final match when he scored for Brazil against Wales in Gothenburg, Sweden, on June 19, 1958. At 17 years, 239 days old, he was hailed as a Brazilian hero. They nicknamed him the *Perola Negra* ("Black Pearl").

TENNIS

In 1985, BORIS BECKER (b. 1967), of West Germany, became the youngest Wimbledon champion when he won the tournament at the age of 17 years, 227 days.

GET SPORTY!

Tees, baskets, field goals, and nets! How many ways can you win a set? Brush up on your knowledge of some of our favorite pastimes.

BASEBALL

Nobody can really be sure when baseball began in America, but some say the game started in Cooperstown, New York (home of the National Baseball Hall of Fame and Museum), in 1839. It was first played professionally in 1869, and since then the sport has grown to thirty teams in two leagues (the American and National Leagues). The regular baseball season stretches from April through September, with the two best teams (one from each league) making it to the World Series in October. The World Series is a best-of-seven showdown, alternating between the two teams' hometowns, that determines who takes home the title of champion.

TENNIS

Tennis was first played in France as early as the twelfth century, when players knocked a ball around a walled-in court with the palms of their hands. The game gradually developed the use of paddles and then racquets to hit a ball over a net. These days it's played with high-tech racquets on one of three surfaces: clay, grass, or cement. Unlike team sports, tennis has no "season," but goes year round, all over the world. There are countless tournaments and events for players to establish their rankings, but as for Grand Slams, there are only four: the Australian Open in Melbourne (January), the French Open, near Paris (May), Wimbledon, in London, England (July), and the U.S. Open in New York City (September). The game itself has a very unusual scoring system: players score points to win games; to win a set, a player must win at least six games and lead his or her opponent by two games. The player who wins the most sets (usually two out of three) wins the match!

BASKETBALL

Basketball is, without a doubt, the zoomingest game on television. From start to finish, the players zigzag across the court, leaping to make baskets and whipping the ball through the air. The game was invented in 1891 by a Massachusetts gym teacher, Dr. James Naismith. Basketball moves almost without stopping and it is made up of four periods, each 12 minutes long. The twenty-nine teams in the National Basketball Association (NBA) play from October to June, with the best teams from the Eastern and Western Conferences going head to head in a best-of-seven playoff at the end.

FOOTBALL

American football's origins can be found in the rough British sport of rugby, which was brought over to the United States in the mid-1800s. The boys at Harvard College changed some rules (including the use of a new egg-shaped ball) and called it "football," but it wasn't until 1880 that a student at Yale came up with the rules for modern football. The rules have continued to change over the years, as have the setup of leagues, conferences, and so forth. Currently there is only one league—the National Football League (NFL)—divided into the American and National Football Conferences. The cream of these crops play each other in the hyped-up extravaganza known as the Super Bowl—one game, held in January. The regular season lasts from September to early January, with the thirty-two teams playing just one game per week. If you've ever watched a football game and seen how brutal it can be, you can understand why!

GOLF

Golf began in fourteenth-century (1300s) Scotland, where the rolling green hills, grazed clean by sheep, were ideal for knocking a little ball around. This very landscape is the model for modern golf courses around the world, set in deserts, along coasts, and among forests. Because it's spread out all over the planet, golf is in swing year round, with the best players coming out to compete on courses that are both challenging and beautiful. One tournament, the Pebble Beach Pro-Am (which stands for "Professional-Amateur"), held in southern California, attracts Hollywood stars who play alongside the pros. Some, like comedians Bill Murray and Ray Romano, have turned the tournament into more than just a sporting event with their goofy antics on the course.

SOCCER

The early history of modern soccer resembles the history of the British Empire. Before the codification of official Football Association laws (which made no mention of the allowable number of players or the duration of play), soccer games were disorganized conflicts with fields as large as towns, and as many as 500 participants involved in a brutal daylong conflict. During the late nineteenth century, however, Britain began taking the game to various parts of the world, along with the two other English favorites, cricket and rugby.

Of the three, soccer has become the most popular international sport. By the second Olympic Games, which were held in Paris in 1900, soccer had already been introduced as a demonstration game. Eight years later, England defeated Denmark in the first official Olympic soccer final during the 1908 London Games. The world governing body for soccer, Fédération Internationale de Football Association (FIFA), held its first meeting in 1904 in Paris. It was attended by seven member nations. Today, the fact that FIFA's international membership has swelled to over 150 national associations—rivaled only by the International Olympic Committee—gives testament to soccer's enduring legacy.

VOLLEYBALL

Most volleyball enthusiasts will place the birthplace of beach volleyball in Santa Monica, California, some time in the early 1920s. Families played in teams of six on courts set up on the beach. The first two-man beach volleyball game was also played in Santa Monica in 1930, and in 1947, the first official two-man beach tournament was held at State Beach, California. In fact,

the sport can trace most of its major developments in the Golden State, but its Santa Monica heritage didn't keep it from attaining international scope. At the 1996 Atlanta Olympic Games, with twenty-four men's teams and sixteen women's teams representing their countries, beach volleyball became an official tournament event.

ICE HOCKEY

Ice hockey began about 200 years ago when schoolboys in Windsor, Nova Scotia, Canada, took the Irish game of hurling, changed the rules around, and played it on the ice of a favorite local skating pond. Since 1904, when a league was formed in the United States, ice hockey has been a professional sport, with thirty teams competing across the States and Canada. The regular season starts up in October and lasts all winter long. It winds down in April, but playoffs among the best teams extend through May. The Stanley Cup Playoffs, ice hockey's final series, are held in June.

MUHAMMAD ALI (b. 1942) first achieved fame when he won a gold medal in boxing at the 1960 Olympics. Later, he became the first man to win the heavyweight title three times. Ali was fast and graceful, and outside of the boxing ring, "The Greatest" was known for his witty rhymes and poetry. More than that, though, Ali was both appreciated and scorned for his anti-war beliefs, standing up for his Islamic religion, and his willingness to have boxing matches in faraway places to make people aware of other countries and cultures.

JIM BROWN (b. 1936) is one of football's great legends. A fullback for the Cleveland Browns from 1957 to 1966, Brown was known for his power and speed. He scored 126 touchdowns, 106 of them by rushing. He led the NFL in rushing for eight of the nine years he played. Brown retired at 30, to become an actor and start an organization to help young people.

WAYNE GRETZKY (b. 1961) began skating on the frozen river near his grandparents' farm when he was only 2. Like many kids in Canada, he grew up watching and playing hockey during much of his free time. Gretzky is considered the most influential professional hockey player of all time, and when he retired in 1999, he held sixty-one National Hockey League records.

MICHAEL JORDAN (b. 1963) is probably the greatest basketball player ever to play the game. Before becoming a pro, Michael attended the University of North Carolina and was twice voted College Player of the Year. While in school, he also helped the U.S. win a gold medal in basketball at the 1984 Olympics. Jordan went on to become a superstar for the Chicago Bulls and has helped them win six national championships. He has been awarded the Most Valuable Player trophy five times.

BABE RUTH (1895–1948) was so difficult as a child that his parents sent him to a home run by Catholic brothers when he was 7. It was there that he learned to play baseball. He learned so well that he was famous citywide

by 19, and signed up by the Orioles. Later, he went to the Boston Red Sox to play, and finally to the New York Yankees. This bigger-than-life national hero played a total of twenty full seasons, leading the league in home runs twelve times, in runs eight times, in RBIs six times, and in slugging thirteen times.

TIGER WOODS (b. 1975) is one of golf's all-time most successful players. When he was only 2, he was on TV putting with the comedian Bob Hope. At 3, he scored an unbelievable 48 on nine holes. At 15, he was the youngest ever to win the U.S. Junior Amateur; at 18, the youngest ever to win the U.S. Amateur; and at 21, the youngest Masters Golf Tournament champion. Tiger has won forty-two tournaments, and became the first person ever to hold all four professional major championships at the same time.

FREDERICK DOUGLASS (1817–95), the son of a black slave woman and a white man, escaped slavery himself when he was twenty-one. One day he was asked to speak in front of a group of abolitionists, or people against slavery, about his experiences. From that time on, he would continue to give speeches and write articles and books about equal rights among people of all colors. He advised Abraham Lincoln and even recruited black soldiers for the North's Union Army during the Civil War. He is considered by many to be the founder of the American Civil Rights movement.

MOHANDAS "MAHATMA" K. GANDHI (1869–1948) was born in India, but his parents sent him to England to study law. He then moved to South Africa, where he became a champion of the rights of Indian immigrants who were mistreated by local society. It was there that Gandhi first came up with the idea of using passive resistance instead of violence against injustices. When he returned to India, he led the Indian National Congress and took up the struggle of achieving independence from Britain, which ruled over the country. Ultimately, Gandhi and his nonviolent ways triumphed for India's freedom. Many years later, his name is still an international symbol of progress achieved through peaceful methods.

MARTIN LUTHER KING, JR. (1929–68) was a minister in Montgomery, Alabama, in 1955 when a black woman, Rosa Parks, took a stand against unfair rules by refusing to sit in the back of the bus just because of her color. Right after that, King led a boycott of city buses, which resulted in black people being able to legally sit anywhere they wanted. King later headed up peaceful demonstrations against racism that generated lots of attention—enough attention to cause the creation of the Civil Rights Act to protect people no matter their color. In 1963, he led a Civil Rights march on Washington, D.C., that brought together more than 200,000 people. The refrain of his most famous speech, about his

HEROES OF PEACE

hopes for racial harmony, was "I have a dream." In 1964, King was awarded the Nobel Peace Prize.

NELSON MANDELA (b. 1918) was one of the leading figures of a political organization called the African National Congress. He studied law and was actively opposed to apartheid, which was a policy that gave black people lesser rights than whites in South Africa. From 1964 to 1990, Mandela was kept in jail for opposing the government and its unjust laws; instead of disappearing, however, he became a symbol all over the world for resisting racism. In 1993, Mandela and the president who released him shared the Nobel Peace Prize. A year later, Nelson Mandela was elected the first black president of South Africa.

Superheroes!

We love superheroes! They capture our hearts and imagination with their daring, amazing, and heroic deeds. They fly, stretch, and swing through the air to save the world from destruction practically every day. Their superpowers amaze and delight us. Which one is your *favorite*?

Batman & Robin

Batman has no special powers, just a big brain, an undying hatred of criminals, and lots of cool toys. Rich playboy Bruce Wayne sees his parents get murdered when he is just a boy, and ever since then devotes his life to battling the criminal element in Gotham City. Aided by his sidekick, Robin, and their faithful butler, Alfred, as well as his gadgets—most famous, the Batmobile—Batman takes on his nemeses, including the Joker, Two-Face, the Penguin, and Catwoman.

Captain Marvel

Captain Marvel's origins are as a humanoid alien named Mar-Vell from a race called the Kree. With his powerful golden Nega-Bands (worn on the wrists), he is able to exchange atoms with teenager Rick Jones and take on human form. His powers, thanks to the extraordinary Nega-Bands, include superhuman strength, supersonic speed, and incredible stamina. On top of all that, he has a Cosmic Awareness that allows him to detect invisible beings, objects, and threats anywhere in the universe.

The Fantastic Four

The Fantastic Four are a band of friends who go out into space and come back with superpowers. Reed Richards is the scientist who builds the ship for their expedition; Sue Storm is his fiancée; Johnny Storm is her brother; and Ben Grimm is Reed's old friend.

In space, the four of them encounter a band of poisonous radiation, and when they crash back to earth, they find they have all been transformed. Reed, the leader of the team, becomes Mr. Fantastic. He can expand and stretch his body as if it were made of some kind of gum. Sue becomes the Invisible Girl, and can make herself and any objects she touches invisible. She also is capable of creating a form of mental shield, and has an endless supply of energy. Johnny Storm becomes the Human Torch, able to control fire, shoot it from his fingertips, and even fly through the air in a ball of flame. Ben becomes The Thing, a lumpy, rocky creature with a bad temper. His powers include the ability to withstand extreme heat and cold. Together they form the Fantastic Four.

Flash Gordon

Flash Gordon, an all-American athlete, is kidnapped from Earth and thrust into the middle of a raging war on the distant planet Mongo. Caught between the forces of Prince Barin, the rightful ruler of Mongo, and Ming the Merciless, self-proclaimed emperor of the universe, this ordinary man becomes a hero by displaying extraordinary courage. It is Dr. Hans Zarkov, one of the most brilliant scientists in the world, who forces Flash along with Dale Arden to accompany him on his spaceship to change the course of the approaching Mongo. Dr. Zarkov's scientific prowess has made him an invaluable ally in the fight against Ming. Under Flash's leadership, the oppressed people of Mongo are finally able to rise up and escape Ming's long reign of terror—a deed that Ming has sworn to avenge.

The Hulk

While supervising the trial for an experimental gamma bomb, Dr. Robert Bruce Banner, nuclear physicist, selflessly rushes to the rescue of a teenager who has wandered onto a testing field as the countdown nears zero. He pushes the teenager to safety but is caught in the gamma rays of the blast, and is permanently transformed. At first, Banner changes into a beastly Hulk at sunset and reverts to human form at dawn. After a while, his transformation into the childlike, green Hulk comes to be activated by the release of adrenaline whenever he is intensely excited, no matter what time of day. This 7-foot-tall, thousand-pound, green mass of fury possesses little of

Banner's intelligence or memory, and is so easily enraged that he is a menace to society. You don't want to see him get angry!

Spiderman

Peter Parker, a.k.a. Spiderman, grows up in the house of his uncle Ben and aunt May. An ordinary teenager and a top student at school, Peter Parker gets saddled with superpowers when a radioactive spider bites him. From then on, Peter can climb the sides of buildings and swing through the city on long ropes of web that he shoots from his wrists. Perhaps his most important crime-fighting power is his "spider sense"—the ability to sense and anticipate danger. When a thief murders his uncle Ben during a crime that Spiderman could have prevented, he is racked with guilt. Remembering what his uncle Ben had told him—that with great power comes great responsibility— Spiderman vows to fight all evil until the end of his days. Among his many nemeses are Venom, Carnage, Kraven, and Green Goblin.

Superman

Sent to Earth from his collapsing home planet Krypton by his father, Superman is found and raised by the farmers Jonathan and Martha Kent—who name their new son Clark. Thanks to the Earth's sun, Clark has unbelievable powers. After realizing as a teenager that he is the strongest man on Earth, he uses his powers for good, and to help and protect innocent people!

As a young man, Clark moves to Metropolis, keeping his powers secret from everybody and leading a double life. As Clark Kent, he works for the Daily Planet, the biggest newspaper. When he's not reporting on crime in the city of Metropolis, Kent/Superman is busy fighting it. Very little can stop the Man of Steel—except maybe Kryptonite.

Wonder Woman

Wonder woman is the daughter of Hippolyte, immortal Queen of the Amazons of Paradise Island. Hippolyte molds her daughter out of the clay of Paradise Island and names her Diana, after the Roman name for Artemis, goddess of the hunt. Diana is an exceptional child, displaying incredible strength and agility. She trains in a variety of skills including horsemanship, nursing, and "bullets and bracelets," an Amazon game where the player deflects projectiles with special bracelets.

When Hippolyte holds a contest to select an Amazon to travel to America as a champion of peace, Diana enters and defeats all the other contestants. Hippolyte endows her daughter with a costume and magical implements to represent her people in America. Her tools include her bracelets of submission, a lariat that forces complete honesty and obedience in anyone ensnared, and a jet that is visible only to the eyes of Amazons. With super strength, super speed, and Amazonian skills, Wonder woman is hugely successful in her mission from Amazon, routinely encountering and defeating agents of evil.

A Bag of Tools

by R. L. Sharpe

Isn't it strange
That princes and kings,
And clowns that caper
In sawdust rings,
And common people
Like you and me
Are builders for eternity?

Each is given a bag of tools,
A shapeless mass,
A book of rules;
And each must make—
Ere life is flown—
A stumbling block
Or a steppingstone.

MY SHIP SAILS

Ahoy!

Number of players: four to seven

Setup: The oldest player is the dealer. He deals out seven cards to each player (the extra cards aren't used). Players then arrange their cards by suit (for example, all spades together) and decide which suit they're going to try and collect (they can change their minds as many times as they want, though).

Goal: To be the first to collect seven cards of the same suit

How to play: Each player takes a card he doesn't want and passes it to the right. Cards keep getting passed until someone collects seven cards of the same suit, and yells out, "My ship sails!"

CRAZY EIGHTS

The original "Uno"

Number of players: two to five

Setup: Deal out seven cards to each player and leave the rest facedown in a stack. Take one card from the top of the stack and place it faceup on the table. This will be the discard pile.

Goal: To be the first to get rid of all your cards

How to play: The player to the dealer's left goes first. He looks through his hand for a card that matches the one on the discard pile, either in value (for example, both are Jacks) or suit (both are spades). If he finds one, he places it on top of the discard pile. If the player doesn't have a card that matches, he draws from the deck until he gets one that does match. The exception: Eights are "wild cards"-meaning that you may play them on any card. Whoever plays an 8 of any suit gets to choose the next suit to be played. The winner is the player who gets rid of all his cards first, but the game may continue until there's only one player left standing.

PLAY OR PAY

Who'll get the pot?

Number of players: three to five

Supplies: twenty jellybeans (or toothpicks, buttons, beads, etc.) per player

Setup: The dealer hands out twenty jellybeans to each player, and then deals out the entire deck of cards (it doesn't matter if some players have more cards than others).

Goal: To collect the most jellybeans

How to play: The player to the dealer's left picks a card from his hand and puts it faceup on the table. The player to his left then has to play the next card in the sequence. For example, if the first player played a 3 of spades, the next player has to play the 4 of spades. If a player doesn't have the next card in the sequence, he puts a jellybean into the pot, and it becomes the next player's turn. When the entire suit is played (the card following a King is the Ace of the same suit), the player who

finished it begins a new suit. The first player to run out of cards collects all the jellybeans in the pot. Play as many "rounds" as you like, and the winner is the one with the most jellybeans at the end.

OLD MAID

Don't get stuck with the old fuddy-duddy.

Number of players: three to five

Setup: Remove the Queen of clubs, the Queen of diamonds, and the Queen of spades. Deal out all the cards to the players (it doesn't matter if some players have more than others).

Goal: To avoid becoming the "Old Maid"

How to play: If any player has a pair of matching cards (such as two 7s or two Kings), he discards them on the table. The player to the dealer's left fans out his cards so nobody can see them. He offers them to the player on his left, who pulls one out of the fan without seeing what it is and adds it to his hand. If it makes a pair with anything he has, he discards the pair. That player then lets the next player pick a card from his hand in the same way. The game continues until the only card left is the Queen of hearts, the Old Maid. The player left holding the Old Maid is the loser!

SPIT

A game of speed.

Number of players: two

Setup: Deal out all the cards to both players. Players arrange their cards into five stacks, facedown and solitaire-style (from right to left, the first pile has one card, the second has two, the third has three, and so forth). Turn the top card of each stack faceup. If any top cards match (say two Jacks or three 4s), the player can put them together in a separate stack and turn the next cards up. Each player places his leftover cards in a pile in the middle.

Goal: To be the first to get rid of all your cards

How to play: Players flip over the top cards from their leftover piles into the middle space between them. These are the

"spit" piles. The players then try to get rid of all of their cards from their five stacks into these spit piles as fast as they can, in sequence. Numbers can go up or down (2-3-2-A-K). As each player places faceup cards onto the center piles, the next face-down cards on their stacks are turned face-up. Matching cards can be placed together, and if any stack is finished, a faceup card from another stack can be moved into the empty space, and the card beneath it turned up. (Players are allowed five cards facing up.) If at any time neither player can put any more cards onto the spit piles, both players take the next cards from their leftover piles and place them on their spit piles. When one player has finished all of his stacks, he quickly slaps the spit pile he thinks has fewer cards and takes possession of it—if the other player notices, he can try to slap it first. The players then set up all of their cards again in solitaire-style stacks, and the next round begins. The game ends when one player has discarded all his cards.

GEORGE WASHINGTON (1732–99), known as the "Father of His Country," was born in Virginia, and later became the commander in chief of the Continental Army. After successfully leading his men to victory against the British in the Revolutionary War, he was unanimously elected the first president of the United States. His courage and noble judgment are embodied in a legend from his boyhood. The story goes that young George chopped down his father's prized cherry tree, and even though he faced being punished, he told the truth.

THOMAS JEFFERSON (1743–1826) was the third president of the U.S., but he is also remembered for being an imaginative inventor and architect. Before becoming president, though, he was the main author of the Declaration of Independence, which stated, "all men are created equal" with rights to "life, liberty, and the pursuit of happiness." Jefferson also was largely responsible for making sure that people would always be guaranteed freedom of speech, press, and religion in the Constitution.

ABRAHAM LINCOLN (1809–65) was born in a log cabin, but overcame his humble beginnings by studying and working hard to eventually become the sixteenth president. Shortly after he was elected, the Confederate Southern States left the Union, and the Civil War broke out. Under Lincoln's brave leadership, the country became whole again. He later signed the Emancipation Proclamation, which signaled the beginning of freedom for slaves. His most famous speech was the Gettysburg Address, which beautifully described his hopes for the rebirth of the nation.

FRANKLIN DELANO ROOSEVELT (1882–1945) became the thirty-second president, in 1933, when the United States was suffering through the Great Depression. Roosevelt had a radio show that he often used to calm people down, telling them, "The only thing

PRESIDENTIAL HEROES

we have to fear is fear itself." The president came up with the New Deal, a series of programs and agencies that helped the country get back on its feet again.

JOHN F. KENNEDY (1917–63) became the youngest president, at age 43, in 1961, but not before becoming a World War II hero and winning a Pulitzer Prize for his book *Profiles in Courage*. While in office, he fought for equal rights for African Americans and helped get the space program started. He led the way through some tense times with the Soviet Union and signed a treaty that helped limit the use of missiles and other weapons. Kennedy also was responsible for the Peace Corps, a popular volunteer organization that still brings education and skills to developing countries. His most famous quote is probably, "Ask not what your country can do for you; ask what you can do for your country."

Score!

Next time you want to play a fast and furious game of air hockey, skip the arcade and go for something with a bit of magnetic appeal. With a few basic materials and some creativity, you can make a hockey arena that's sure to be full of action and excitement. Then you can host your own Winter Olympics any time of the year. So grab an opponent and face off!

Extra-large shoebox lid, ruler, colored markers, four paper cups, 3 x 5 index card, scissors, masking tape, rubber bands, 2 bar magnets, 2 chopsticks, 2 metallic washers, red and blue nail polish or paint, plastic button

1. To make your hockey arena, turn the shoebox lid upside down. Draw a straight line across the middle of the lid to create the center court line. Place a paper cup in the middle of the lid and trace the circle to complete the court design.
2. For the goal nets, fold the index card in half lengthwise and cut along the crease. Fold back a 1¼-inch flap on each end of both halves of the index card. Tape flaps to the shoebox lid.
3. Raise the playing field by taping an upside-down paper cup to each corner of the shoebox lid.
4. Use rubber bands to secure a magnet to the end of each chopstick.
5. Paint each washer a different color (red or blue) to identify each team.

TO PLAY: Use the button as a hockey puck and place it in the middle of the court. Place the red and blue washers on either side of the puck. The players hold their chopstick magnets under the shoebox lid to make his washer move on the court. Each player tries to make his washer hit the puck into the goal for one point. The player with the most points after ten minutes wins.

Bugs, Bugs, Bugs

The earth is crawling with some 8 million species of bugs—that's more than any other creature on the planet. And we're still counting! Scientists in Southern Africa recently discovered an entirely new order of insect. Nicknamed the "gladiator bug", it looks something like a mixture of grasshopper, stick insect, and mantis. What if the next new breed of bug lives in your backyard? There's only one way to find out: Grab a net, put on your bug-eyes, and go!

Bug Catcher

Some bugs can be pretty hard to catch without a net. Others are so delicate that we'd squish them if we tried to pick them up. With a good bug net, you can catch all kinds of flyers, buzzers, crawlers, and creepers. No insect expedition is complete without one.

Wire hanger, large plastic bag, wooden dowel or old broom handle, duct tape, tape, screwdriver, hammer, large jar with lid

1. Carefully untwist and bend the coat hanger into a loop no larger than the opening of your plastic bag.
2. Wrap the ends around the end of the broom handle and secure with duct tape.
3. Use tape to fit the edge of the plastic bag around the coat hanger.
4. Use a screwdriver and hammer to poke holes in the jar lid for ventilation. Now you're ready to buzz off for a bug hunt!

Insect Incubator

One of the best ways to learn about bug life is by watching them hatch and grow. Look for places insects might lay eggs, such as trees, shrubs, or underneath moss or bark. Check a local field guide to determine what bugs may be in your area and to help identify their eggs. Be careful not to disturb the eggs once you find them. Gather the twigs, leaves, or bark on which the eggs have been laid. Collect additional similar vegetation that can provide nutrition for the insects once they hatch.

*Egg-laden twigs, cotton, small glass bottle, dirt, water, flowerpot
(4¹/₂ inches in diameter), 2-liter plastic soda bottle,
scissors, cheesecloth, rubber band*

1. Pack the ends of the egg-laden twigs and fresh twigs in cotton and place them in a small bottle of water. Sprinkle a light layer of dirt on top of the water.
2. Place the bottle neck-deep in a flowerpot with dirt. If you've found eggs underneath bark or moss, place those on top of the dirt next to the bottle.
3. You can turn the plastic bottle into a see-through "chimney." Ask an adult to help you cut the neck and the bottom 2 inches off your bottle and discard. Then fit the wider end of the bottle inside the edge of the flowerpot. It should fit snugly.

4. Cover the top of the plastic bottle with cheesecloth and secure in place using the rubber band.
5. Now watch what happens! Depending on the species of eggs, the hatching process may take anywhere from a few days to a few weeks. Keep a journal to record your findings. After the bugs have hatched, take the incubator back to the place where you found the eggs, and carefully release them into the wild.

DOCTOR, DOCTOR

A man walks into a doctor's office and says, "Doctor, Doctor, I think I need glasses." "You certainly do," replies the doctor. "This is a hamburger stand!"

A man walks into a psychiatrist's office and says, "Doctor, you've got to help me. I think I'm a dog!" The psychiatrist replies, "Just lie down here on the couch and tell me all about it." "I can't. I'm not allowed on the furniture!"

"Doctor, Doctor, I have cucumbers growing out of my ears!" "How did this happen?" "Beats me— I planted carrots."

Whad'ya call a boy people walk all over?

Matt.

Whad'ya call a boy who's always asking you for money?

Bill.

Whad'ya call a boy who floats on water?

Bob.

Whad'ya call a boy with a shovel?

Doug.

Whad'ya call a boy without a shovel?

Douglas.

WHAD'YA CALL?

Waiter, what's this fly
doing in my soup?
"Hmm, looks like
the backstroke to me."

Waiter, what's this fly
doing in my soup?
"I think it's drowning, sir."

Waiter, there's a fly
in my soup!
"Okay, I'll bring you a fork."

Waiter, there's a fly
in my soup!
"That's funny. There were
two when I left the kitchen."

Waiter, there's a fly
in my soup!
"Yes sir, we ran
out of spiders."

Waiter, there's a *dead* fly
in my soup!
"Yes sir, it's the hot
water that kills them."

Waiter, there's a fly
in my soup!
"That's *not* a fly sir,
that's just dirt in
the shape of a fly."

WAITER, THERE'S A FLY IN MY SOUP

Pet Trivia

IGUANAS have a dozen or so large pores on the undersides of their thighs. These pores secrete a waxy substance that they use to mark their territory and identify one another.

🐾

HAMSTERS get their name from the German word *hamstern*, which means "to hoard" or "to forage," because they store food in their cheeks, which puff out enormously!

🐾

Though you could probably tell by looking at it, the GUINEA PIG is not a pig. It doesn't come from New Guinea, either! They were probably called "pigs" for their grunts and squeals, and they may have been sold by British sailors, who brought them back from South America in the 1600s, for a guinea (a form of English currency).

🐾

A DOG wags its tail as a way of talking and telling you he is feeling happy. A dog may also wag its tail as a way of communicating with other dogs— one wag might indicate "Hello, how are you?" while another wag might say "I'm the boss around here."

🐾

Have you ever heard of a DEGU? Degus are rodents from Chile that, like some lizards, have the ability to shed their tails if they're caught. Degus, however, will never grow a new one, and their ability to balance will never be the same.

🐾

Earth's first space traveler was a DOG!

🐾

In the wild, IGUANAS like to hang out on tree branches over ponds and streams. This way, if they feel threatened, they simply drop into the water and swim to safety.

🐾

You can tell the age of a young TURTLE by looking at its shell, but not an old turtle. The top of a turtle's shell is divided into sections called shields. On each shield are little circles. In a young turtle, each circle stands for a year's growth—e.g., a two-year-old turtle has two circles

Did you know that ferrets are as smart as dogs?

The oldest gold-fish on record died at the ripe old age of forty-one.

Exotic Pets

BIG CATS: While some people are daring enough to keep tigers, lions, or other huge cats around, those animals need more raw meat than your grocery store can probably handle, and even when they're playing, their size alone makes them quite dangerous. However, some wildcats can be tamed, if you have the money, the space, and the patience! Cats like caracals, servals, bobcats, and lynxes can be trained to use the litter box and get along with other pets just fine.

FERRETS: If a ferret isn't a weasel, and it isn't a rodent, then what is it? Ferrets are totally domesticated animals that are related to (and act a lot like) weasels, which live in the wild. They are as intelligent as dogs and make lively, playful, frisky little friends, but have mischievous, weaselly habits—they love to steal things.

POTBELLIED PIGS: Believe it or not, pigs are very clean animals. They get overheated easily, which is why they're fond of rolling around in the mud. As pets, pigs are smart, can be trained, and can go anywhere with you, just like a dog. However, potbellied pigs grow to be 150 pounds and will knock over anything that isn't nailed down!

IGUANAS: Iguanas may be beautiful, but they sure aren't cuddly. These spiky green reptiles will hang out with the family like the average cat, but need lots more care. For one thing, they are used to hot jungle climates with plenty of places to go swimming. Iguana owners have to provide special lights to keep their pets warm. For another thing, they grow to be about six feet long from end to end, and need lots of space. Many iguana owners devote a whole room to their reptile!

Rabbits should never be picked up by their ears. Ow!

on each shield. After five or ten years, however, you can no longer determine a turtle's age by the circles as they have either become too crowded or have begun to wear off.

Just like cats, RABBITS can get hairballs from grooming themselves—but unlike cats, they can't get rid of them. Feeding your rabbit fresh pineapple juice or pineapple chunks can help prevent hairballs: Pineapple contains an enzyme that helps rabbits digest the hair.

SNAKES can't really be charmed. In India, men called snake charmers play music for cobra snakes, and the cobras seem to dance to it. But in fact snakes are actually deaf. Snake charmers sway and tap on the ground as they play music and the snake feels the vibrations and gets excited, rearing up to strike the charmer. When a cobra is ready to strike, it watches the victim carefully and follows the victim's movements—hence it appears to be swaying to the music.

Some pet rats can be taught to respond to their names.

Pet Posterity

TURTLES: The red-eared slider, which is the most common pet turtle, can live to be 40 years old!

DOGS: In general, the bigger the breed, the shorter its life span. The smallest dogs can live to be 18, and large dogs about 11 or 12.

CATS: The oldest cat on record was 36 when he died in 1936, but that's quite unusual. However, a healthy indoor cat can easily live to be 20.

RABBITS: Most rabbits kept in a safe and clean environment can live to be 10.

LIZARDS: Some lizards, like geckos, can live to be 20.

RODENTS: Gerbils and Syrian (golden) hamsters usually live 2–3 years. Mice live 1–3 years, rats can live 2–4 years, and guinea pigs live the longest—5–7 years.

FISH: Goldfish can live to be 25, if well taken care of.

LEAP FROG

How high can you go?

Number of players: two or more

What you need: a large open area

Everybody stands in a straight line with at least two arms' lengths of space in between each person. Each player crouches in frog position by bending at the knees. Evenly distribute your weight between your hands and feet. Make sure you all have your heads down. Start with the "frog" at the end of the line. He places his hands on the back of the frog in front of him, and leaps over that person with his legs on either side of him. He continues down the line until he's jumped over everybody. Then the new last frog begins jumping, and so on.

116

Fun & Games

SARDINES

Hide-and-seek, but funnier!

Number of players: four or more

What you need: Inside or defined outside space with good hiding spots

Only one person hides. The other players count to a hundred and then search. The first person to find the hider squeezes into the same spot and keeps quiet. The second person to find the hider does the same and so on until only one player is left seeking. The trick is make yourself as skinny as possible and not laugh!

CAPTURE THE FLAG

Get the flag and go!

Number of players: six or more

What you need: 2 white flags, a large open area to run in (a soccer field is ideal), tape or chalk to mark boundaries

The object of the game is to capture the other team's flag. Mark the side and end lines of the field, a dividing line in the middle, two endzones, and a jail near each endzone. Place a flag in each endzone. Divide players into two teams. Each team occupies their half of the field. Players must run through the opposing team's territory, grab their flag, and get it back across the midline without being tagged. Tagged players must go to jail. Jailed players must stay in jail unless they are tagged by an untagged teammate and freed. Players are not allowed to hang out at their endzones guarding their flag. Game is over when a flag is captured or if all of a team's players are in jail.

Worm Farm

Imagine having five hearts, eating your weight in food every day, breathing through your skin, and spending most of your time digging around in dirt. That's what it's like to be a worm. These wriggly critters have the Midas touch with garbage. They can turn it into nitrogen-rich soil, which is worth its weight in gold to plants, gardeners, and farmers. You can turn your old apple peels and egg-shells into "pay dirt" with a little help from some night crawlers that you care for in a worm farm.

Lidded container (preferably plastic) about 18-inches wide x 12 inches long x 12 inches high, newspaper, bowl of water, soil, food scraps, large stirring stick, a dozen or more red worms (also called red wigglers or night crawlers) found outdoors among decomposing leaves or at a bait shop

1. Ask a parent to poke several small holes in the lid and sides of your container for air.
2. Rip several pages of newspaper into strips and soak in a bowl of water. Squeeze the excess water out of the paper and fill your bin about halfway.
3. Sprinkle a thin layer of soil on top of the damp newspaper.
4. Add small scraps of food to the bin and turn the mixture over a few times (do this every time you add food).
5. Add your worms. Keep your bin in a cool spot away from direct sunlight, like the basement or garage. Make sure the bedding stays moist but not soggy.
6. Watch the worms do their stuff. Feed them a little bit every day, or a few times

a week. Avoid overfeeding by checking to see that the worms have eaten food scraps before giving them more. You'll know you're not feeding them enough if they look pale and stringy.

Worm Juice

After a month or so, the worm bedding turns into humus, a natural fertilizer that comes from the worms' liquid and solid waste. You can harvest the humus by feeding the worms on one side of the bin for a while. They'll migrate to that side, and you can remove the humus using a big spoon or scoop. Repeat steps 2 and 3 to refill this side of your bin. Start feeding on the "new" side again to entice your worms so you can harvest the other side also. Humus is rich stuff, so you don't need much to fertilize your soil.

Happy Meals

DO feed your worms coffee grounds and filters, tea bags, fruit and vegetable scraps, eggshells, cereal, bread

DON'T feed your worms onions, garlic, meat, fat, grease, dairy, or non-organic matter

Gone Fishin'

Worms reproduce every few weeks. So, before long, you'll have plenty of bait to go catch the big one.

Some of the best things in life come in bite sizes. This ultimate recipe for nachos ups the ante for plain old chips & dip. Served hot with beans and melted cheese, it's practically a meal unto itself. Potato skins are equally good, and you can spice them up with a dash of red pepper sauce or salsa. For larger snack appetites, sink your teeth into Cheesy Pizza Bread. And for a hot snack that you don't have to bake, try these flavored popcorn recipes. Just right for a night at home watching movies.

CHEESY POTATO SKINS

2 medium-size baking potatoes
2 tablespoons butter, softened
1 cup cheddar cheese, grated
4 slices bacon, cooked and crumbled
1/4 cup sour cream
2 tablespoons black olives, chopped
2 tablespoons chives, finely chopped (optional)

1. Preheat oven to 425°F.
2. Scrub potatoes well and pierce with a fork. Bake on bottom rack for 1 hour, or until tender when tested with fork. Let potatoes cool enough to handle.
3. Cut potatoes in half lengthwise. With large spoon, scoop out center of each potato, leaving a shell thickness of about 1/2 inch. (store scooped-out potato in container for another use).
4. Quarter potato halves. Then cut quarters in half to create sixteen triangular wedges. Arrange potato skins on cookie sheet.
5. Brush insides of potato skins with butter and bake 8–12 minutes, or until golden and crispy. Remove from oven.
6. Sprinkle potato skins with cheese and bake for another 5 minutes, or until cheese melts.
7. Sprinkle crumbled bacon on top of each skin. Add a dollop of sour cream and top with olives and chives. Serve while hot.

Makes 16 skins.

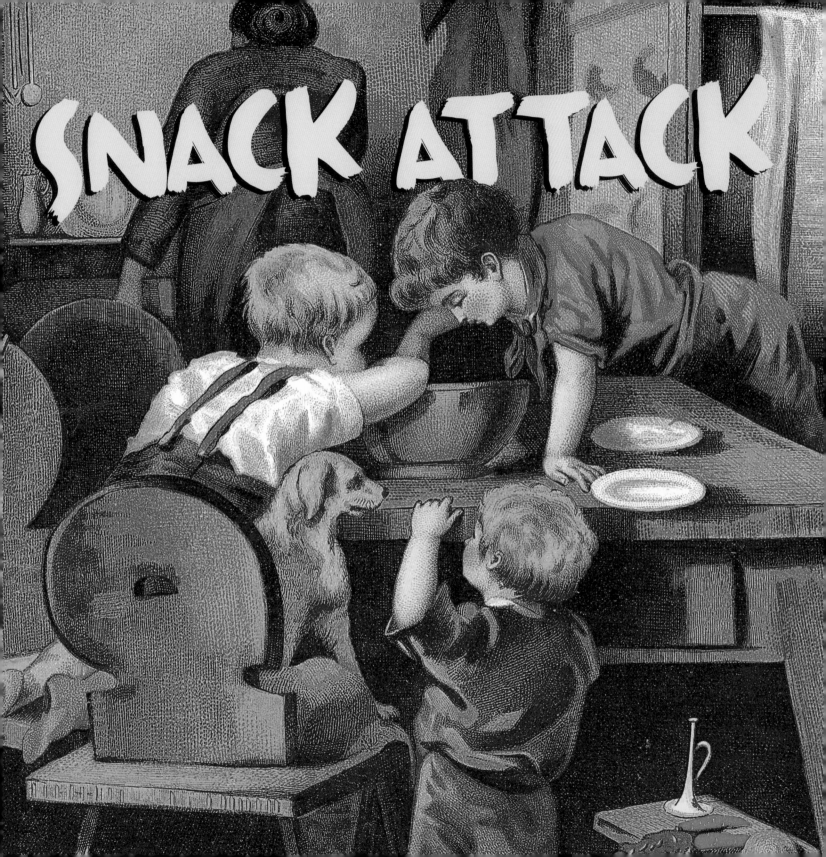

SUPER NACHOS

1 16-ounce can refried beans
1 tablespoon taco seasoning
2 cups tomatoes, diced
2 tablespoons cilantro, minced
2 avocados
2 teaspoons lemon juice
1 8- to 10-ounce bag tortilla chips
1/4 lb. grated Monterey Jack cheese
1/4 lb. grated cheddar cheese
8 ounces sour cream
3 jalapeño peppers (optional), minced

1. Preheat oven to 400°F.
2. In a saucepan, mix refried beans and taco seasoning. Cook over medium heat until bubbly. Remove from heat.
3. In a small bowl, combine tomatoes and cilantro until well blended.
4. In a separate bowl, mash avocados with lemon juice until well blended.
5. Arrange chips evenly on a large cookie sheet or ovenproof platter. Spread a layer of refried beans on chips. Sprinkle grated cheese over beans. Spread tomatoes evenly on top. Bake 3–5 minutes, or until cheese is melted.

6. Spoon avocado mixture on top of nachos. Top with sour cream. Sprinkle with sliced chilies if desired. Eat immediately!

Makes 8 to 10 servings.

CHEESY PIZZA BREAD

2 (8-ounce) packages cream cheese, softened
1 1/4 cups sour cream
1 cup shredded mozzarella cheese
1/2 cup shredded cheddar cheese
1 cup pizza sauce
2/3 cup chopped red bell pepper
1/2 cup sliced green onions
1 teaspoon dried oregano
1/2 teaspoon crushed red pepper flakes
1/4 teaspoon minced garlic
1 loaf crusty French bread

1. Preheat oven to 350°F.
2. In a medium baking dish, combine all the ingredients except bread.
3. Bake 5 minutes, or until bubbly and lightly browned. Remove from oven.
4. While sauce is cooling, place crusty bread in oven for 2 minutes—don't let it burn!
5. Spoon your warm pizza sauce onto bread and enjoy.

Makes 2 servings.

POPCORN TOPPERS

Toss one quart of popcorn with any of these fun flavors:

TEX-MEX POPCORN

1 teaspoon chili powder
1 teaspoon paprika
1 teaspoon cumin
2 tablespoons melted butter

CINNAMON POPCORN

1 tablespoon sugar
1 1/2 teaspoons cinnamon
2 tablespoons melted butter

CHOCOLATE POPCORN

1/4 cup sugar
1 1/2 teaspoons cocoa powder
1 1/2 teaspoons butter
2 tablespoons evaporated milk
1/8 teaspoon vanilla

Combine all ingredients in a saucepan and bring to a boil, stirring frequently. Pour over popcorn and toss.

ZESTY POPCORN

4 tablespoons grated Parmesan cheese
1 tablespoon Italian seasoning
4 teaspoons melted butter

CHEESY POPCORN

4 tablespoons grated sharp cheese
4 teaspoons melted butter
1/2 teaspoon garlic salt

MEXICAN POPCORN

2 tablespoons melted butter
1 tablespoon taco seasoning

Around the World in Eighty Days is a classic adventure novel by the

French writer Jules Verne (1828-1905), first published in 1873. In the story,

Phileas Fogg of London and his newly-employed French valet named

Passepartout attempt to circumnavigate the entire world in eighty days on

a wager of £20,000 set by Phileas Fogg's friends at the Reform Club. The

wager originated from an argument among friends at the Reform Club

when an article from London's *Daily Telegraph* was passed around, stating

that with the opening of a new railway section in India it was suddenly

possible to travel around the world in eighty days, via railway and steamer

ships. Phileas Fogg and his young valet Passepartout come to realize that

the trip is not as easy as they expected, and are forced along their journey

to think of creative solutions to more than a few compromising situations.

Phileas Fogg had not concealed from Sir Francis his design of going round the world, nor the circumstances under which he set out; and the general only saw in the wager a useless eccentricity and a lack of sound common sense. In the way this strange gentleman was going on, he would leave the world without having done any good to himself or anybody else.

The train stopped, at eight o'clock, in the midst of a glade some fifteen miles beyond Rothal, where there were several bungalows, and workmen's cabins. The conductor, passing along the carriages, shouted, "Passengers will get out here!"

Phileas Fogg looked at Sir Francis Cromarty for an explanation; but the general could not tell what meant a halt in the midst of this forest of dates and acacias.

Passepartout, not less surprised, rushed out and speedily returned, crying: "Monsieur, no more railway!"

"What do you mean?" asked Sir Francis.

"I mean to say that the train isn't going on."

Around the World in Eighty Days
by Jules Verne

The general at once stepped out, while Phileas Fogg calmly followed him, and they proceeded together to the conductor.

"Where are we?" asked Sir Francis.

"At the hamlet of Kholby."

"Do we stop here?"

"Certainly. The railway isn't finished."

"What! not finished?"

"No. There's still a matter of fifty miles to be laid from here to Allahabad, where the line begins again."

"But the papers announced the opening of the railway throughout."

"What would you have, officer? The papers were mistaken."

"Yet you sell tickets from Bombay to Calcutta," retorted Sir Francis, who was growing warm.

"but the passengers know that they must provide means of transportation for themselves from Kholby to Allahabad."

"No doubt," replied the conductor; "but the passengers know that they must provide means of transportation for themselves from Kholby to Allahabad."

Sir Francis was furious. Passepartout would willingly have knocked the conductor down, and did not dare to look at his master.

"Sir Francis," said Mr. Fogg quietly, "we will, if you please, look about for some means of conveyance to Allahabad."

"Mr. Fogg, this is a delay greatly to your disadvantage."

"No, Sir Francis; it was foreseen."

"What! You knew that the way—"

"Not at all; but I knew that some obstacle or other would sooner or later arise on my route. Nothing, therefore, is lost. I have two days, which I have already gained, to sacrifice. A steamer leaves Calcutta for Hong Kong at noon, on the 25th. This is the 22nd, and we shall reach Calcutta in time."

There was nothing to say to so confident a response.

"Monsieur, I think I have found a means of conveyance."

It was but too true that the railway came to a termination at this point. The papers were like some watches, which have a way of getting too fast, and had been premature in their announcement of the completion of the line. The greater part of the travellers were aware of this interruption, and, leaving the train, they began to engage such vehicles as the village could provide four-wheeled palkigharis, waggons drawn by zebus, carriages that looked like perambulating pagodas, palanquins, ponies, and what not.

Mr. Fogg and Sir Francis Cromarty, after searching the village from end to end, came back without having found anything.

"I shall go afoot," said Phileas Fogg.

Passepartout, who had now rejoined his master, made a wry grimace, as he thought of his magnificent, but too frail Indian shoes. Happily he too had

been looking about him, and, after a moment's hesitation, said, "Monsieur, I think I have found a means of conveyance."

"What?"

"An elephant! An elephant that belongs to an Indian who lives but a hundred steps from here."

"Let's go and see the elephant," replied Mr. Fogg.

Phileas Fogg, without getting in the least flurried, then proposed to purchase the animal outright, and at first offered a thousand pounds for him. The Indian, perhaps thinking he was going to make a great bargain, still refused.

Sir Francis Cromarty took Mr. Fogg aside, and begged him to reflect before he went any further; to which that gentleman replied that he was not in the habit of acting rashly, that a bet of twenty thousand pounds was at stake, that the elephant was absolutely necessary to him, and that he would secure him if he had to pay twenty times his value. Returning to the Indian, whose small, sharp eyes, glistening with avarice, betrayed that with him it was only a question of how great a price he could obtain. Mr. Fogg offered first twelve hundred, then fifteen hundred, eighteen hundred, two thousand pounds. Passepartout, usually so rubicund, was fairly white with suspense.

At two thousand pounds the Indian yielded.

"What a price, good heavens!" cried Passepartout, "for an elephant."

"What a price, good heavens!" cried Passepartout, "for an elephant."

It only remained now to find a guide, which was comparatively easy. A young Parsee, with an intelligent face, offered his services, which Mr. Fogg accepted, promising so generous a reward as to materially stimulate his zeal. The elephant was led out and equipped. The Parsee, who was an accomplished elephant driver, covered his back with a sort of saddle-cloth, and attached to each of his flanks some curiously uncomfortable howdahs. Phileas Fogg paid the Indian with some banknotes which he extracted from the famous carpet-bag, a proceeding that seemed to deprive poor Passepartout of his vitals. Then he offered to carry Sir Francis to Allahabad, which the brigadier gratefully accepted, as one traveller the more would not be likely to fatigue the gigantic beast. Provisions were purchased at Kholby, and, while Sir Francis and Mr. Fogg took the howdahs on either side, Passepartout got astride the saddle-cloth between them. The Parsee perched himself on the elephant's neck, and at nine o'clock they set out from the village, the animal marching off through the dense forest of palms by the shortest cut.

...at nine o'clock they set out from the village, the animal marching off through the dense forest of palms by the shortest cut.

MUST-READ BOOKS

In addition to the favorite titles excerpted in this book, here are other well-loved stories to add to your reading list. Happy reading!

THE BOOK OF THREE by Lloyd Alexander
Taran, would-be hero and assistant pig keeper, assembles a group of companions to rescue the oracular pig Hen Wen from the forces of evil. One book in the five Prydian Chronicles.

THE CRICKET IN TIMES SQUARE by George Selden
A fast-talking mouse and a city-wise cat welcome a country cricket to a new home in a NYC subway station.

ENCYCLOPEDIA BROWN: BOY DETECTIVE by Donald Sobol
The first in a series of detective stories in which the reader is challenged to match wits with the 10-year-old mastermind of Idaville's war on crime.

HARRY POTTER AND THE SORCERER'S STONE by J. K. Rowling
The first book in a series of tales about a young wizard in training. From kids to adults, no one can get enough of Harry and his magical adventures.

MUST-READ BOOKS

THE HOBBIT by J. R. R. Tolkien

A completely normal, happy hobbit is not pleased when a wizard knocks on his front door looking for an adventurer, but this small upset turns into a grand quest with trolls, giant spiders, and magic rings.

HOW TO EAT FRIED WORMS by Thomas Rockwell

Would you eat fifteen worms in fifteen days for fifty dollars? Billy intends to do so in order to buy the minibike he's been dreaming of.

JAMES AND THE GIANT PEACH by Roald Dahl

After a terrible rhinoceros accident takes away his parents, poor James is forced to live with his horrible aunt and uncle until a bag of magic crystals changes his life.

MANIAC MAGEE by Jerry Spinelli

After his parents die, Jeffrey Lionel Magee's life becomes legendary, as he accomplishes athletic and other feats that hold his contemporaries in awe. 1991 Newbery Award.

TREASURE ISLAND by Robert Louis Stevenson

Some walk the plank, and some find buried treasure, while young Jim Hawkins tries to survive the infamous Long John Silver in this sweeping pirate epic.

WELCOME TO DEAD HOUSE, GOOSEBUMPS NO. 1 by R. L. Stine
In this first book of the popular Goosebumps series, two children are thrilled when their father inherits an old house-that is, until they realize that it's haunted.

THE WIND IN THE WILLOWS by Kenneth Grahame
Join Badger, Mole, Rat, and Toad as they struggle between the quiet, easy way of the River Bankers and the boisterous, excitable Wild Wooders.

Lemuel Gulliver is an average man of average intelligence. A gentle ship's surgeon, he serves as narrator of *Gulliver's Travels*. Over the course of the narrative, the unsophisticated storyteller makes four journeys to "remote nations of the world." Below are excerpts from his initial two voyages— among the most fantastic and memorable adventures in all of English literature. Gulliver first sets sail aboard the *Antelope*, and he and his shipmates encounter a deadly storm. Shipwrecked in Lilliput, Gulliver discovers the pocket-sized Lilliputians (one twelfth Gulliver's size) with their enormous egos. The next voyage, this time aboard the Adventure, sees Gulliver abandoned by the ship's crew at Brobdingnag, where the inhabitants are ten times his size! In *Gulliver's Travels*, Jonathan Swift (1667–1745) created an ingenious work of remarkable wit and texture. Upon publication in 1726, *Gulliver* was read by children for the inventive story and by adults for the political satire. More than 275 years later, the tale of imaginary voyages continues to draw a following for both its simplicity and multiple layers of meaning; its playfulness in the face of a grim vision of humanity; its marvelous fantasy worlds and the relative realism of its characters.

A Voyage to Lilliput

I lay down on the Grass, which was very short and soft, where I slept sounder than ever I remember to have done in my Life, and, as I reckoned, above Nine Hours; for when I awakened, it was just Daylight. I attempted to rise, but was not able to stir: For as I happen'd to lye on my Back, I found my Arms and Legs were strongly fastened on each Side to the Ground; and my Hair, which was long and thick, tied down in the same Manner. I likewise felt several slender Ligatures across my Body, from my Armpits to my Thighs. I could only look upwards; the Sun began to grow hot, and the Light offended my Eyes. I heard a confused Noise about me, but in the Posture I lay, could see nothing except the Sky. In a little time I felt something alive moving on my left Leg, which advancing gently forward over my Breast, came almost up to my Chin; when bending my Eyes downwards as much as I could, I perceived it to be a human Creature not six Inches high, with a Bow and Arrow in his hands, and a Quiver at his Back. In the meantime, I felt at least Forty more of the same Kind (as I conjectured) following the first. I was in the utmost Astonishment, and roared so loud, that they all ran back in a Fright; and some of them, as I was afterwards told, were hurt with the Falls they got by leaping from my Sides upon the Ground. However, they soon returned, and one of them, who ventured so far as to get a full Sight of my Face,

Gulliver's Travels
by Jonathan Swift

lifting up his Hands and Eyes by way of Admiration, cried out in a shrill but distinct Voice, *Hekinah Degul*: the others repeated the same Words several times, but I then knew not what they meant. I lay all this while, as the Reader may believe, in great Uneasiness; At length, struggling to get loose, I had the Fortune to break the Strings, and wrench out the Pegs that fastened my left Arm to the Ground; for, by lifting it up to my Face, I discovered the Methods they had taken to bind me, and at the same time, with a violent Pull, which gave me excessive Pain, I a little loosened the Strings that tied down my Hair on the left Side, so that I was just able to turn my Head about two Inches. But the creatures ran off a second time, before I could seize them; Whereupon there was a great Shout in a very shrill Accent, and after it ceased, I heard one of them cry aloud, *Tolgo Phonac*; when in an Instant I felt above a Hundred Arrows discharged on my left Hand, which pricked me like so many Needles; and besides they shot another Flight into the Air, as we do Bombs in Europe, whereof many, I suppose, fell on my Body (though I felt them not) and some on my Face, which I immediately covered with my left

Hand. When this Shower of Arrows was over, I fell a groaning with Grief and Pain, and then striving again to get loose, they discharged another Volly larger than the first, and some of them attempted with Spears to stick me in the Sides; but, by good Luck, I had on me a Buff Jerkin, which they could not pierce. I thought it the most prudent Method to lie still, and my Design was to continue so till Night, when, my left Hand being already loose, I could easily free myself: And as for the Inhabitants, I had Reason to believe I might be a Match for the greatest Armies they could bring against me, if they were all of the same Size with him that I saw.

I perceived it to be a human Creature not six Inches high, with a Bow and Arrow in his hands, . . .

A Voyage to Brobdingnag

One of the Reapers approaching within ten Yards of the Ridge where I lay, made me apprehend that with the next Step I should be squashed to Death under his Foot, or cut in two with his Reaping hook. And therefore when he was again about to move, I screamed as loud as Fear could make me. Whereupon the huge Creature trod short, and looking round about under him for some time, at last espied me as I lay on the Ground. He considered a while with the Caution of one who endeavours to lay hold on a small dangerous Animal in such a Manner that it shall not be able either to scratch or to bite him, as I myself have sometimes done with a Weasel in England. At length he ventured to take me up behind by the

Middle between his fore Finger and Thumb, and brought me within three Yards of his Eyes, that he might behold my Shape more perfectly. I guessed his Meaning, and my good Fortune gave me so much Presence of Mind, that I resolved not to struggle in the least as he held me in the Air, about sixty Foot from the Ground, although he grievously pinched my Sides, for fear I should slip through his Fingers. All I ventured was to raise my Eyes towards the Sun, and place my Hands together in a supplicating Posture, and to speak some Words in an humble melancholy Tone, suitable to the Condition I then was in. For I apprehended every moment that he would dash me against the Ground, as we usually do any little hateful Animal which we have a mind to destroy. But my good Star would have it, that he

At length he ventured to take me up behind by the Middle between his fore Finger and Thumb, . . .

appeared pleased with my Voice and Gestures, and began to look upon me as a Curiosity, much wondering to hear me pronounce articulate Words, although he could not understand them. In the mean time I was not able to forbear groaning and shedding Tears, and turning my Head towards my Sides; letting him know, as well as I could, how cruelly I was hurt by the Pressure of his Thumb and Finger. He seemed to apprehend my Meaning; for, lifting up the Lappet of his Coat, he put me gently into it, and immediately ran along with me to his Master, who was a substantial Farmer, and the same Person I had first seen in the Field.

STAR GAZERS

The night sky looks different in Nome, Alaska, from the way it looks in Miami, Florida. And the stars will be in a different place in the summer night skies from where they are in the winter, spring, or fall. You may know how to spot the Big Dipper and Orion's Belt, but do you know how to find Pegasus, the flying horse, or Draco the dragon? Here's an easy way to make your own star chart. Then you can try to map out constellations as they appear from your backyard.

Star chart, aluminum foil, straight pins, 2-liter plastic soda bottle, scissors, black construction paper, tape, penlight

1. Place the star chart over the shiny side of a piece of aluminum foil. With a straight pin, poke a tiny hole through each major star so that the pin goes through the foil. When you're done, the foil should be a replica of the major stars in your star chart.
2. Ask an adult to help you cut the bottom off the soda bottle. Wrap the bottle in construction paper and tape it in place.
3. Cover the bottom of the soda bottle with the aluminum foil. Make sure that the shiny side of the foil faces the inside of the bottle. Tape the foil in place.
4. Look through the mouth of the bottle. The pinpricks of light should be a good representation of the night sky. Try shining a penlight through the mouth of the bottle in a dark room and casting your stars against the wall. You can use your star map to identify the constellations. Then on the next clear night, go outside and try out your star gazer bottle to help find the real constellations.

The next time you're in the mood for something sweet, whip up one of these easy and mouth-watering beverages.

BANANA BAVARIA SHAKE

1 cups milk
2 ripe bananas
2 scoops chocolate ice cream

Combine all ingredients in a blender and mix until smooth.

Makes 2 servings.

PURPLE COW

1 12-ounce can frozen grape juice
3 cups milk

Place ingredients in a blender and mix until smooth and frothy.

Makes 4 servings.

ROOT BEER FLOAT

24 ounces (2 cans) root beer
4 scoops vanilla ice cream or frozen yogurt

1. Pour root beer evenly into four tall glasses.
2. Drop a scoop of ice cream or frozen yogurt into each glass. The ice cream will fizz and develop an icy crust.

3. Serve with sundae spoons and straws and slurp immediately!

Makes 4 servings.

PEANUT À LA MOO

1/2 cup chunky peanut butter
2 cups milk
4 scoops vanilla ice cream

Put all ingredients in a blender. Pulse a few times until consistency is frothy. Be careful not to overblend. Pour in sundae glasses and serve with a straw.

Makes 4 servings.

CITRUS GINGER FIZZ

1/2 cup lemon juice
1/4 cup lime juice
1 teaspoon powdered sugar
1 tablespoon sugar
16 ounces seltzer
4 lime slices

1. In a large pitcher, combine lemon juice, lime juice, powdered sugar, and sugar. Stir with a wooden spoon until blended.
2. Add seltzer and stir again.
3. Pour into tall glasses over ice cubes and serve with lime slices.

Makes 4 servings.

Pinhole Camera

The word photography *comes from the Greek term meaning "light writing." In ancient times, people learned that light passing through a pinhole would cast images into a dark room. The word* camera *comes from the Latin word for "room." By the 1700s, people discovered that certain chemical combinations turned dark when exposed to sunlight. Soon, they would learn to combine the use of cameras and chemically treated plates to make photographs. By making your own pinhole camera, you will have a chance to see up close (and upside down!) how images can be "written" in light. Then, on the next sunny day, see what develops!*

Marker, cylindrical potato-chip can or tennis-ball can with clear plastic lid, utility knife, duct tape, aluminum foil, pushpin

1. Carefully draw a circle around the circumference of the can about two inches from the bottom.
2. Ask an adult to cut your can in two pieces along the line. The edges should be smooth and even.
3. Remove the plastic lid from the top of the can and cover the newly cut shorter portion.
4. Tape the can back together with duct tape. Try to make the two segments fit as snugly as possible.
5. To avoid getting any light in your pinhole camera, cover the entire can in duct tape.
6. With the pushpin, carefully poke a pinhole in the center of the bottom of the can.
7. Go to a well-lit or sunny area and look in the open end of the can. You may need to cup your hand around your eye to prevent additional light from getting inside the tube. Light that enters through the pinhole will project an upside down image on the plastic lid inside the tube. Now you've got an eye for photography!

Light-Bulb Telegraph

Dit-dit-dit, dah-dah-dah, dit-dit-dit. You may recognize that as international Morse code for SOS. But you don't have to be a captain, a pilot, or a secret agent to send codes to your friends. You can make a telegraph by creating a simple electrical circuit, and be flashing messages in no time!

Telephone wire, wire stripper, block of wood or strip of cardboard, masking tape, 5 metal paper clips, flashlight bulb, D-cell battery, bulb holder (optional: available at hardware stores)

1. Start by cutting three lengths of wire. Strip an inch of the plastic insulation from each of the ends.
2. Use wood or cardboard to make the base for your telegraph. Secure the light bulb onto the base with masking tape. Spread open two paper clips. Take two wires and wrap an end of each around the inner fold of each clip. Wrap both clips around the base of the light bulb. Make sure the clips are contacting the metal base. Tape clips in place.
3. Wrap one end of the wires around a paper clip and tape to the negative (flat) end of the battery. Tape the battery in place onto your telegraph base.
4. Wrap the end of the other wire (connected to the bulb) around a

thumbtack, under the head, and press into the telegraph base to secure.

5. Take the remaining piece of wire and wrap each end around a paper clip. Attach one clip to the positive (knobby) end of the battery and secure it in place with tape. Touch the other paper clip to the thumbtack. This completes the circuit and lights the bulb. (If your bulb doesn't light up, check your connections!) Secure the paper clip to the base with another thumbtack.

6. To make a circuit breaker, bend the paper clip slightly apart so that it no longer touches the thumbtack connected to the light-bulb wire. Then, simply tap the clip to the thumbtack to complete the circuit and start sending secret messages!

Morse Code

Tap and release quickly to make a dot. Tap, hold, and release to make a dash.

A .−	I ..	Q −−.−	Y −.−−	7 −−...
B −...	J .−−−	R .−.	Z −−..	8 −−−..
C −.−.	K −.−	S ...	1 .−−−−	9 −−−−.
D −..	L .−..	T −	2 ..−−−	0 −−−−−
E .	M −−	U ..−	3 ...−−	, (comma) −−.−−
F ..−.	N −.	V ...−	4 ....−	. (period) .−.−.−
G −−.	O −−−	W .−−	5	? ..−−..
H	P .−−.	X −..−	6 −....	

MUST-SEE MOVIES!

THE 5,000 FINGERS OF DR. T (1953) stars Hans Conried, Tommy Rettig. Bart uncovers Dr. Terwilliker's crazy plan to force five hundred boys to practice at his gigantic piano twenty-four hours a day, seven days a week, in this live-action Dr. Seuss story.

A CHRISTMAS STORY (1983) stars Melinda Dillon, Darren McGavin, Peter Billingsley. A boy's only Christmas wish is for a Red Ryder BB gun in this hilarious story about the fun and craziness of Christmas in 1940s America.

THE ADVENTURES OF ROBIN HOOD (1938) stars Errol Flynn, Basil Rathbone, Olivia de Havilland. The first great action-adventure movie pits the courageous Robin and his Merry Men against the evil Prince John and Guy of Gisbourne.

BACK TO THE FUTURE (1985) stars Michael J. Fox, Christopher Lloyd. Eighties teenager Marty McFly travels back in time to the 1950s in order to save Doc Brown's life, but ends up causing more trouble when he stops his parents from meeting. Unless Marty can get his parents to fall in love, he becomes in danger of being erased from all time in this special-effects masterpiece.

CITY LIGHTS (1931) stars Charlie Chaplin. In this silent comedy, a tramp helps a beautiful poor blind girl he has fallen in love with. The boxing match in this film is one of Chaplin's funniest scenes.

DUCK SOUP (1933) stars the Marx Brothers. Crazy Groucho becomes president of the bankrupt country Freedonia and ends up starting a war with neighboring

Sylvania over the hand of Mrs. Teasdale. Harpo and Chico only add to the rising insanity in this satire of war, politics, and basically everything.

E. T.: THE EXTRA TERRESTRIAL (1982) stars Henry Thomas, Drew Barrymore. A group of children must protect a space alien from being captured, and send him back to his home planet.

JURASSIC PARK (1993) stars Sam Neil, Jeff Goldblum, Laura Dern, Richard Attenborough. Watch out, here comes the velociraptor! Millionaire Richard Attenborough asks two paleontologists and a mathematician to advise him on his cloned dinosaur theme park. Unfortunately, the dinosaurs escape! Amazing special affects and hair-raising suspense make this Steven Spielberg blockbuster one to watch.

THE KARATE KID (1984) stars Ralph Macchio, Pat Morita. Mr. Miyagi teaches Daniel-san martial arts when the boy moves to his neighborhood. Daniel learns the power of friendship and gains confidence as he overcomes school bullies and enters a karate competition.

KING KONG (1933) stars Fay Wray. A film crew discovers a gigantic ape on Skull island. Unfortunately, the ape falls in love with the film's female star. When the captured Kong is brought back to New York, the love-crazed monkey goes ape in the Big Apple. A true film classic with amazing stop-motion animation.

THE NEVERENDING STORY (1984) stars Barret Oliver. A young boy finds a magical book about a fantastic world in great danger. He learns to believe in himself and his own powerful imagination in his effort to save it.

PEE-WEE'S BIG ADVENTURE (1985) stars Paul Reubens. The very strange Pee-wee goes on a cross-country journey to recover his precious stolen bike. Along the way, he encounters ghosts, movie stars, convicts, and other hilarious characters.

MUST-SEE MOVIES!

THE PRINCESS BRIDE (1987) stars Cary Elwes, Robin Wright, Billy Crystal. A funny fairy-tale story, with some quirky twists, about a beautiful princess and her brave hero, with some giants, miracle men, and an evil prince thrown in.

STAGECOACH (1939) stars John Wayne. This is the quintessential Western movie, with plenty of action, gunfights, and savage Indians. The Ringo Kid must protect the fragile stagecoach passengers as they make their way across the American West.

STAR WARS (1977) A true sci-fi gem! The Jedi Knight Ben (Obi-Wan) Kenobi enlists the help of the young Luke Skywalker, the roguish Han Solo, and the very hairy Chewbacca to restore the beautiful Princess Leia to her throne and to destroy the Death Star. The one that started it all.

WALLACE & GROMIT: THE WRONG TROUSERS (1993) An evil penguin uses Wallace and his fantastic mechanical trousers invention to commit a robbery. Its up to Gromit, Wallace's faithful dog, to save the day in this amazing animated short.

WHITE FANG (1991) stars Ethan Hawke. Jack London's famous adventure story about the friendship between a boy and a wolf-dog takes place during the exciting Yukon gold rush in the early 1900s.

WILLY WONKA AND THE CHOCOLATE FACTORY (1971) stars Gene Wilder. Charlie wins a chance to tour the tastiest factory in the world in this wonderful musical based on Roald Dahl's book.

THE WIZARD OF OZ (1939) stars Judy Garland. The classic story has Dorothy Gale on the road to Emerald City, looking for the Wizard of Oz in order to get back to her home in Kansas. Along the way, she meets the Scarecrow, the Lion, and the Tin Man, and battles the Wicked Witch of the West.

Additional favorites: *Superman; Old Yeller: Bringing Up Baby; Rookie of the Year*

One...Two... Three...Juggle!

Learn how to dazzle your friends with a trick that's been around for centuries! Whether you're entertaining kings and queens or kids and teens, you'll have as much fun showing off your new talent as your audience will have watching you. Once you get the hang of it, you'll be able to toss around all kinds of objects—just make sure they're not breakable!

Three balls, apples, or beanbags

1. Start with one ball. Toss it gently back and forth from one hand to the other. Try and make the ball arc at about eye level. Practice several times until your tosses are smooth and consistent. Tip: When you throw from right to left, try to make the ball arc in front of your left ear. When you throw from left to right, try to make the ball arc in front of your right ear.

2. Get ready for two balls! Have one ball in each hand. Using your right hand, toss the first ball in the air. When it reaches the highest point of its arc, toss the second ball (from your left hand to your right). When the second ball starts to arc, catch the first ball (with your left hand). Hold it. Then catch the second ball (with your right hand). Hold it. The trick is to make sure the balls don't hit each other in the air. Now try again, starting this time with your left hand instead of your right. Continue to practice until you can do several tosses in a row without dropping the balls.

3. Now for the tricky part: the third ball. Start by holding two balls in your right hand and one in your left. Toss the first ball in your right hand toward the left. When the ball arcs, toss the ball in your left hand toward the right. Catch the first ball in your left hand. As the second ball arcs, throw the last ball with your right hand toward your left. Catch the second ball with your right hand. Then catch the last ball in your left hand. Try it again starting with two balls in your left hand. Once you get the hang of it, see how many times in a row you can do it without dropping any balls.

Sweet Feats

LARGEST MILKSHAKE

Manhattan's Ira Freehof, who has the unique distinction of owning the celebrated Comfort Diners, also broke the record for world's largest milkshake on August 1, 2000, with a 6,000-gallon classic Black & White shake that shattered the previous record of 4,603.24 gallons.

1¢ EA

LARGEST LOLLIPOP Jolly Rancher presented the world's largest lollipop when it unwrapped its giant-sized replica of its regular cherry lollipop on June 25, 2002. At an exceptionally large 4,016 pounds and measuring over 5 feet square and 18.9 inches thick, the giant sucker broke the old record by more than 1,000 pounds.

LARGEST CHOCOLATE MODEL The largest chocolate model ever built weighed 8,818 pounds, 6 ounces, and was in the shape of a traditional Spanish sailing ship. Put into commission in February 1991 by the Gremi Provincial de Pastisseria, Confiteria i Bolleria school in Barcelona, the chocolate vessel measured 42 feet, 8 inches by 27 feet, 10 $\frac{1}{2}$ inches by 8 feet, 2$\frac{1}{2}$ inches.

LARGEST BUBBLE-GUM BUBBLE Measured under the strict rules of the fiercely competitive activity of bubble-gum bubble blowing, the largest diameter for a bubble was 23 inches, by Susan Montgomery Williams of Fresno, CA, on July 19, 1994.

TALLEST CAKE The tallest cake ever created measured a whopping 101 feet, 2$\frac{1}{2}$ inches high. Made by Beth Cornell Trevorrow with a team of helpers at the Shiawassee County Fairgrounds, MI, it had one hundred tiers, the last of which was finished on August 5, 1990.

CHARLIE CHAPLIN (1889–1977) will always be remembered for the original and comedic antics he performed, wearing his signature black derby hat, a ragged suit, and a little moustache, while sporting a cane. Though he came from a poor English family, Charlie made it big in America and ultimately directed his own films and even started his own movie studio. People still consider him one of the funniest and most talented actors and filmmakers of all time.

LEONARDO DA VINCI (1452–1519) created great paintings, like "Mona Lisa" and "The Last Supper." Leonardo was more than a painter, though—he was also a sculptor, architect, scientist, and inventor. He kept amazingly detailed notebooks full of things—from sketches of the human body to designs for flying machines. Anyone who is very good at many things is called a Renaissance man, which Leonardo was.

WOLFGANG AMADEUS MOZART (1756–91) is generally considered the greatest musical genius of all time. He started to play the harpsichord at age 3 and compose music at 5. When he was only 9, he wrote an entire symphony. As a young boy, he traveled from his home in Austria to play the keyboard and the violin in royal courts across Europe. This young Austrian grew up to create some of the most beloved sonatas, symphonies, and concertos of all time. His operas *The Marriage of Figaro* and *The Magic Flute* are still performed all over the world today.

PABLO PICASSO

(1881–1973) Pablo Picasso is probably the most famous artist of the twentieth century. Born in Spain, this son of an art teacher eventually created more than twenty thousand works over seventy-five years. While most artists have one style and stick to it, Picasso went through many, including neo-impressionism, his "Blue Period," and his "Rose Period." His most famous style, though, was Cubism, in which he used geometrical shapes to represent natural forms. His passion for art also found its way into sculpture, prints, ceramics, and stage design. Pablo Picasso is often thought of as the father of modern art.

WILLIAM SHAKESPEARE

(1564–1616) was born in Stratford-upon-Avon, England, on April 23, and even though he is the greatest playwright who ever lived, much of his life is a mystery. People guess that he must have had a good education because so many of his plays and so much of his poetry are full of Latin, Greek, and classical mythology. Unlike many artists, Shakespeare was extremely popular in his day, and people flocked to his plays. Audiences today still thrill to the sound of the beautiful language and the daring action of *Hamlet*, *Romeo & Juliet*, and *The Tempest*.

HEROES OF THE ARTS

Are You Lucky?

160

Don't break a mirror – 7 years of bad luck!

Do you flinch with a black cat crosses your path? Do you find yourself staring at the sidewalk, tiptoeing over the cracks? Do you carry a rabbit's foot in your pocket? Boy, you're superstitious. Still not lucky enough? Here are more things to try. Good luck!

- Get out of bed on the same side you got in to avoid bad luck •

Cross your fingers • Find a four-leaf clover • Carry an acorn

- Spit on a new bat for good luck before using it for the first time •

Hang a horseshoe above your doorway • Don't walk under a ladder

- Pick up a penny if it's heads side up, don't touch if it's tails up!

- If you spill salt, throw it over your left shoulder to avoid bad luck

- Don't open an umbrella in the house • For a lucky fishing

day throw back the first fish you catch •

Don't leave your shoes upside down!

Airplane

Humans have always dreamed of flying. Beginning in 1505, Leonardo da Vinci (1452-1519) studied the flight of birds and tinkered with ideas for flying machines. So how did we get from da Vinci's drawings to our 747 jet planes? How can a heavier-than-air (as much as 870,000 pounds at takeoff) vehicle with a carrying capacity of 600 plus people get off the runway?

The most basic (yet troublesome) principle to grasp about flying is that air has atmosphere—air is a gas is a liquid. This is important to understand because it is the constant pressure of this "liquid" around the plane, and particularly the wings, that keeps a plane aloft.

There are four basic aerodynamic forces. They are lift, weight, thrust, and drag. *Lift* is generated when air particles split at the edge of the wing, either going over or under the wing.

Because of the curved shape on top of the wing, the particles traveling over the top travel faster than those at the bottom. Faster-moving air has lower pressure than slow-moving air. The greater pressure under the wing forces the wing up. When lift surpasses weight, the aircraft "lifts off."

Like lift and weight, thrust and drag work together. The propellers or jet engines of a plane create thrust. Like a household fan, air is moved over the blades. Air's resistance to an object moving through it creates drag. Just as your hand feels pressure when you hold it out of the window of a moving car, so a plane "feels" pressure as it moves through the air. When there is more thrust than drag on a plane, it speeds up.

Hot-Air Balloon

It looks like a huge parachute attached to a basket, so what keeps a hot-air balloon from falling to the ground? Well, the huge piece of synthetic fabric shaped like a bulb is called an *envelope*. A balloon is also equipped with a burner and a basket. When not in use, a hot-air balloon's envelope is limp. To get the balloon to fly, the operator fills the envelope with hot air using the propane gas in the burner. Once the balloon is upright, the passengers—some balloons can fly with up to ten—pile into the basket. The operator then continues to heat the air inside the envelope (to about 100° C) until it expands enough to force a

quarter of the total air out the base of the envelope. When the weight of the balloon is reduced to less than its *upthrust*, it takes off. The operator has no real means to steer the balloon, but can keep it at a constant height with intermittent blasts from the burner. The balloon drifts with the wind until the burner is cut off. Air in the envelope cools and contracts, and more cool air is able to enter into the envelope. This weighs the balloon down, causing it to descend. The operator uses short bursts of the burner to create a soft landing.

What lies at the bottom of the ocean and twitches?

A nervous wreck.

When do ghosts usually appear?

Just before someone screams.

What is the difference between a jeweler and a jailer?

One sells watches and the other watches cells.

What do you call a chicken at the North Pole?

Lost.

THAT'S FUNNY!

Why do dragons sleep during the day?
So they can fight knights.

What is black and white, black and white, black and white?
A penguin caught in a revolving door.

What do you get when you cross a shark with a parrot?
An animal that talks your head off.

How do you say good-bye to a vampire?
Immediately.

Why did the mayonnaise blush?
It saw the salad dressing!

What should you do if a wild elephant charges you in the jungle?
Pay him, dummy!

Model Artist . . . Or Bust!

Do you have an eye for art? What about a nose . . . or an ear? Many of the world's greatest artists, including Pablo Picasso, Alberto Giacometti, and Auguste Rodin regularly used themselves as models for their creations. With a little papier-mâché you can be well on your way to sculpting your own likeness, too.

Shoebox, cardboard paper-towel tube, scissors, tape, balloon, newspaper, flour, water, bowl, tempera paints, paintbrushes, mirror (optional)

1. To make the frame for the neck and shoulders, cut a hole in the middle of the top of the shoebox just wide enough for the paper-towel tube to fit through. Slip the tube in the hole so that it touches the bottom of the box. Secure it with tape. You may want to cut a few inches off the top of the tube to shorten the neck.
2. For the head, blow up the balloon and tie the end in a knot. Set the knot end on top of the tube and tape it in place.
3. Prepare the papier-mâché by ripping up several pieces of newspaper into thin strips. Then, mix flour and water together in a bowl to make a runny paste.
4. One by one, dip strips of newspaper in the flour solution and cover the head, neck, and shoulders with several layers of paper.
5. To add lips, eyebrows, cheekbones,

ears, nose, chin, and hair, dip a few strips of newspaper in the flour mixture and form them into the shape you want. Then paste it in place on the bust. Try looking at yourself in the mirror as you work. Or ask a friend to model for you!

6. When the papier-mâché has dried, brush on finishing touches with tempera paint.

Bust Buster

You can turn your finished and dried sculpture into a piñata with a few simple changes.

Scissors, candy, tape, string, baseball bat or stick

1. Cut the neck off, leaving a couple of inches below the head.
2. Stick the scissors through the tube to burst the balloon. Fill the head cavity with candy. Then make two or three vertical cuts along the neck and fold the flaps against the head, closing the cavity. Tape them shut.
3. Poke two holes at the top of the head about an inch apart. Thread the string through the holes and tie a knot. Now you can hang your piñata from a tree or on the end of a pole and have your friends take whacks at it to break the candy loose!

Not all pies need to bake in the oven and cool on the windowsill. These recipes call for easy cookie crusts and chilling instead of baking. You can mix and match the pie crusts with the fillings for variety. Once you discover how easy these pies are to make, you may need to have your friends over for a pie-eating contest!

BANANA CREAM PIE

FOR CRUST:

1 1/2 cups chocolate graham crackers,
    finely crushed
4 tablespoons confectioners' sugar
1 teaspoon cinnamon
6 tablespoons butter, melted

Mix crushed graham crackers, sugar, cinnamon, and melted butter until well blended. Press crumb mixture into 10-inch pie plate. Freeze for one hour.

FOR FILLING:

2/3 cup sugar
1/3 cup flour
1/4 teaspoon salt
2 cups milk
3 egg yolks, slightly beaten
2 tablespoons butter
2 teaspoons vanilla
2 ripe bananas
whipped cream

1. In medium saucepan combine sugar, flour, and salt. Stir in milk with wooden spoon and cook over medium heat until mixture starts to bubble and thicken. Remove from heat.
2. Stir in egg yolks until mixture is smooth. Cook again over medium heat for about two minutes until mixture comes to a boil, stirring constantly. Remove from heat.
3. Stir in butter and vanilla.
4. Cover surface of creme mixture with plastic wrap or wax paper so that skin doesn't form on top. Cool to room temperature.
5. Slice bananas and arrange them in pastry shell. Pour creme filling on top and chill for 4 to 6 hours.
6. Serve with whipped cream.

Makes 8 to 10 servings.

CHOCOLATE PEANUT-BUTTER PIE

FOR CRUST:

1^1/$_2$ cups vanilla wafers, finely crushed
2 tablespoons confectioners' sugar
6 tablespoons butter, melted

Mix crushed cookies, sugar, and melted butter until well blended. Press crumb mixture into 10-inch pie plate. Freeze for one hour.

FOR FILLING:

6 tablespoons cream cheese
6 tablespoons peanut butter
^{1}/$_2$ cup confectioners' sugar
^{3}/$_4$ cup non-dairy whipped topping
1 package instant chocolate pudding
1^3/$_4$ cup milk
whipped cream
chocolate sprinkles

1. In large bowl, beat cream cheese and peanut butter until fluffy. In two to three stages, gradually add confectioners' sugar and whipped topping and continue to beat until smooth and creamy. Spoon into pie crust and freeze for 30 to 60 minutes, until firm.

2. In medium bowl, combine instant pudding and milk. Beat with fork until smooth. Spoon on top of peanut-butter layer and freeze an additional 30 to 60 minutes until firm.

3. Serve with whipped cream and garnish with chocolate sprinkles.

Makes 8 to 10 servings.

STRAWBERRY ICE CREAM PIE

FOR CRUST:

1^1/$_2$ cups Oreo cookies, finely crushed
3 tablespoons butter, melted

Mix cookie crumbs and butter until well blended. Press crumbs firmly into pie plate.

FOR FILLING:

2 cups strawberry ice cream, softened
2 cups vanilla ice cream, softened
16 ounces frozen strawberries, thawed with juice
16 large marshmallows
1 cup heavy (whipping) cream
^{1}/$_4$ cup sugar

1. Fill bottom of pie crust with strawberry ice cream. Freeze until firm (about 30 minutes).

2. Add layer of vanilla ice cream on top of strawberry layer. Freeze again until firm (about 30 minutes).
3. In saucepan, combine marshmallows with 2–3 tablespoons juice from strawberries. Stir over medium heat until melted.
   OR: In micro-wavable bowl, coat marshmallows with juice from strawberries and microwave on high for about 1¹/₂ minutes or until melted. Cool.
4. Fold strawberries into cooled marshmallows. Spread mixture onto pie over vanilla ice-cream layer. Freeze again until firm.
5. Whip cream and sugar until stiff. Spoon onto top layer of pie. Serve cold.

Makes 8 to 10 servings.

MOCHA-TOFFEE ICE-CREAM PIE

FOR CRUST:
1¹/₂ cup Oreo cookies, finely crushed
3 tablespoons butter, melted

Mix cookie crumbs and butter until well blended. Press crumbs firmly into 9-inch pie plate.

FOR FILLING:
2 cups coffee ice cream, softened
12 ounces caramel topping
2 cups chocolate ice cream, softened
2 cups nondairy whipped topping, thawed
1 English toffee bar, crumbled

1. Spoon coffee ice cream into crust and spread evenly. Freeze until firm, about 15 minutes.
2. Spread half of the caramel topping on top of the coffee ice cream.
3. Spread chocolate ice cream on top of the caramel layer. Freeze until firm, about 15 minutes.
4. Spread the remaining caramel topping on top of the pie. Arrange dollops of whipped topping in a circular pattern on top of the caramel layer and sprinkle with crumbled toffee bar. Freeze pie until firm, at least 5 hours.
5. Allow pie to stand at room temperature at least 15 minutes before serving.

Makes 8 to 10 servings.

THE OAK

by Alfred Tennyson

Live thy Life,
Young and old,
Like yon oak,
Bright in spring,
Living gold;

Summer-rich
Then; and then
Autumn-changed,
Soberer-hued
Gold again.

All his leaves
Fallen at length,
Look, he stands,
Trunk and bough,
Naked strength.

Glass Garden

What if you could explore a rain forest or check out a desert landscape—without ever leaving your room? You can if you build a terrarium. All you need to get started is a goldfish bowl or a fish tank and you can capture a mini ecosystem. Take some time to learn about the plants you'd like to grow, so you can be sure you're giving them the right kind of soil and light. The reptile area of your local zoo or a nearby botanical garden can be a great place to get ideas.

Marbles or pebbles, large glass container, charcoal (from aquarium or pet shop), potting soil, decorative rocks and figurines (optional), Plexiglas lid (optional)

1. Place a layer of pebbles about 2 inches deep in the glass container to allow for good drainage.
2. Cover the pebbles with a layer of charcoal. This helps keep the soil "sweet." Then add a few inches of potting soil. *Tip: If you add a few worms to the soil, they'll make food for the plants and add life to your terrarium! If you're planning an arid landscape, choose soil that is sand based.*
3. Arrange small plants, decorative rocks, and figurines. Depending on the types of plants you choose, temperature and water requirements will vary.
4. When the plants get too big, ask an adult to help you transplant them outdoors, and start anew!

DESERT Cacti and succulents usually thrive on plenty of light and dry heat. Water is still important, but add it very sparingly—about once every month or two months should be sufficient.

TROPICAL Orchids and carnivorous plants generally like a warm, humid atmosphere. You can create a more controlled environment by covering the terrarium with a Plexiglas lid. This will recycle the water and allow condensation to build up on the sides of the glass.

WOODLAND Bark, moss varieties, and many ferns do well in cooler, shady conditions. Indirect light is often ideal. These plants like water, but if you see condensation building up on the glass, you'll know you're giving them too much.

KNOCK, KNOCK!

Knock, knock!
> Who's there?

Manuel.
> Manuel who?

Manuel be sorry if
you don't open up
quick!

Knock, knock!
> Who's there?

Sherwood.
> Sherwood who?

Sherwood like to
come in.

Knock, knock!
> Who's there?

Harry.
> Harry who?

Harry up and open up!

Knock, knock!
> Who's there?

Lewis.
> Lewis who?

Lewis my keys and can't get in.

Knock, knock!
> Who's there?

Matthew.
> Matthew who?

Matthews are wet, can I come in and dry them?

WHO'S THERE?

IDIOMS

An idiom is a figurative expression, used in a particular language, that only makes sense within the context of its entire sentence.

A chip on one's shoulder "You have a chip on your shoulder" means that you are harboring resentment or hostility, or are overly sensitive over a shortcoming.

An arm and a leg "This costs an arm and a leg" means that the item costs a large amount of money.

All ears "I'm all ears" means that I am giving you my undivided attention.

All thumbs "I'm all thumbs" means that I'm clumsy, not very good with my hands.

Beat around the bush "Don't beat around the bush" means to get directly to the point.

Biting off more than one can chew "You're biting off more than you can chew" means you are trying to deal with too big a responsibility—or too many things—at once.

What do these idioms mean?

- At the drop of a hat • His bark is worse than his bite • Bend over backwards •
- Call it quits • Can of Worms • Dance to a different drummer • Far cry •
- Face the music • Get a move on • Hands are tied • If worst comes to worst •
- Land on one's feet • Make fun of • Off the deep end • Pain in the neck •
- Raining cats and dogs • Tail between one's legs • Up one's sleeve •
- Don't waste your breath • You're telling me •

PALINDROMES

A palindrome is a word that is spelled the same way backward and forward:

civic	madam	radar
dad	mom	refer
deed	noon	reviver
did	nun	rotor
eve	peep	stats
ewe	pop	tat
eye	pullup	toot
kayak	pup	tot
level	racecar	wow

Can you create a sentence that is a palindrome? These sentence can be read backwards and forwards. Here's are some examples:

> Was it a car or a cat I saw?
>
> Step on no pets.
>
> Rise to vote, sir.
>
> Madam, I'm Adam.
>
> Never odd or even.
>
> Too bad, I hid a boot.

One of the most famous palindromes is "A man, a plan, a canal—Panama!" by Leigh Mercer, 1914.

Word Fun!

Along the banks of the Hudson River, near Tarrytown, New York, sits the small village of Sleepy Hollow. Its inhabitants, primarily Dutch colonists, are a superstitious lot. They often spend their evenings sharing stories of the resident ghouls and goblins of their drowsy town. Sleepy Hollow's newest member, gawky Ichabod Crane, has come to town to teach the children. He often finds himself listening to their marvelous stories. The favorite and most ghastly story of all is that of the Headless Horseman. It is said that the horrific ghost rides through town after dark in search of his missing head! One evening at a country ball, Ichabod unsuccessfully woos the girl of his fancy, Katrina Van Tassel. Dejected, he mounts his horse, Gunpowder, and decides to head home. . . . Washington Irving (1783–1859) wrote *The Legend of Sleepy Hollow* in 1820. It was originally published as the sixth installment of Irving's *The Sketch Book of Geoffrey Crayon*, Gent., and became an instant classic. *The Sketch Book* also included Irving's celebrated tale "Rip Van Winkle" (1819). These stories, set in early-nineteenth-century rural America, were fashioned from German folktales. They were the first American works to gain international fame.

It was the very witching time of night that Ichabod, heavy-hearted and crest-fallen, pursued his travel homewards, along the sides of the lofty hills which rise above Tarry Town, and which he had traversed so cheerily in the afternoon. The hour was as dismal as himself. Far below him, the Tappan Zee spread its dusky and indistinct waste of waters, with here and there the tall mast of a sloop riding quietly at anchor under the land. In the dead hush of midnight he could even hear the barking of the watch-dog from the opposite shore of the Hudson; but it was so vague and faint as only to give an idea of his distance from this faithful companion of man. Now and then, too, the long-drawn crowing of a cock, accidentally awakened, would sound far, far off, from some farm-house away among the hills—but it was like a dreaming sound in his car. No signs of life occurred near him, but occasionally the melancholy chirp of a cricket, or perhaps the guttural twang of a bull-frog, from a neighboring marsh, as if sleeping uncomfortably, and turning suddenly in his bed.

All the stories of ghosts and goblins that he had heard in the afternoon, now came crowding upon his recollection. The night grew darker and darker; the stars

The Legend Of Sleepy Hollow

by
Washington Irving

seemed to sink deeper in the sky, and driving clouds occasionally hid them from his sight. He had never felt so lonely and dismal. He was, moreover, approaching the very place where many of the scenes of the ghost stories had been laid. In the center of the road stood an enormous tulip tree, which towered like a giant above all the other trees of the neighborhood, and formed a kind of landmark. Its limbs were gnarled, and fantastic, large enough to form trunks for ordinary trees, twisting down almost to the earth, and rising again into the air. It was connected with the tragical story of the unfortunate André, who had been taken prisoner hard by; and was universally known by the name of Major André's tree. The common people regarded it with a mixture of respect and superstition, partly out of sympathy for the fate of its ill-starred namesake, and partly from the tales of strange sights and doleful lamentations told concerning it.

All the stories of ghosts and goblins that he had heard in the afternoon, now came crowding upon his recollection.

As Ichabod approached this fearful tree, he began to whistle: he thought his whistle was answered,—it was but a blast sweeping sharply through the dry branches. As he approached a little nearer, he thought he saw something white, hanging in the midst of the tree,—he paused and ceased whistling; but on looking more narrowly, perceived that it was a place where the tree had been scathed by lightning, and the white wood laid bare. Suddenly he heard a groan,—his teeth chattered and his knees smote against the saddle: it was but the rubbing of one huge bough upon another, as they were swayed about by the breeze. He passed the tree in safety; but new perils lay before him.

About two hundred yards from the tree a small brook crossed the road, and ran into a marshy and thickly wooded glen, known by the name of Wiley's swamp. A few rough logs, laid side by side, served for a bridge over this stream. On that side of the road where the book entered the wood, a group of oaks and chestnuts, matted thick with wild grapevines, threw a cavernous gloom over it. To pass this bridge was the severest trial. It was at this identical spot that the unfortunate André was captured, and under the covert of those chestnuts and vines were the sturdy yeomen concealed who surprised him. This has ever since been considered a haunted stream, and fearful are the feelings of the schoolboy who has to pass it alone after dark.

As he approached the stream, his heart began to thump; he summoned up, however, all his resolution, gave his horse half a score of kicks in the ribs, and attempted to dash briskly across the bridge; but instead of starting forward, the perverse old animal made a lateral movement, and ran broadside against the fence. Ichabod, whose fears increased with the delay, jerked the reins on the other side, and kicked lustily with the contrary foot: it was all in vain; his steed started, it is true, but it was only to plunge to the opposite side of the road into a thicket of brambles and alder bushes. The schoolmaster now bestowed both whip and heel upon the starveling ribs

This has ever since been considered a haunted stream.

of old Gunpowder, who dashed forward, snuffling and snorting, but came to a stand just by the bridge, with a suddenness that had nearly sent his rider sprawling over his head. Just at this moment a plashy tramp by the side of the bridge caught the sensitive ear of Ichabod. In the dark shadow of the grove, on the margin of the brook, he beheld something huge, misshapen, black, and towering. It stirred not, but seemed gathered up in the gloom, like some gigantic monster ready to spring upon the traveler.

The hair of the affrighted pedagogue rose upon his head with terror. What was to be done? To turn and fly was now too late; and besides, what chance was there of escaping ghost or goblin, if such it was, which could ride upon the wings of the wind? Summoning up, therefore, a show of courage, he demanded in stammering accents—"Who are you?" He received no reply. He repeated his demand in a still more agitated voice. Still there was no answer. Once more he cudgelled the sides of the inflexible Gunpowder, and, shutting his eyes, broke forth with involuntary fervor into a psalm-tune. Just then the shadowy object of alarm put itself in motion, and, with a scramble and a bound, stood at once in the middle of the road. Though the night was dark and dismal, yet the form of the unknown might now in some degree be ascertained. He appeared to be a horseman of large dimensions, and

The schoolmaster now bestowed both whip and heel upon the starveling ribs of old Gunpowder, who dashed forward, snuffling and snorting.

mounted on a black horse of powerful frame. He made no offer of molestation or sociability, but kept aloof on one side of the road, jogging along on the blind side of old Gunpowder, who had now got over his fright and waywardness.

Ichabod, who had no relish for this strange midnight companion, now quickened his steed, in hopes of leaving him behind. The stranger, however, quickened his horse to an equal pace. Ichabod pulled up, and fell into a walk, thinking to lag behind,—the other did the same. His heart began to sink within him; he endeavored to resume his psalm-tune, but his parched tongue clove to the roof of his mouth, and he could not utter a stave. There was something in the moody and dogged silence of this pertinacious companion, that was mysterious and appalling. It was soon fearfully accounted for. On mounting a rising ground, which brought the figure of his fellow traveler in relief against the sky, gigantic in height, and muffled in a cloak, Ichabod was horror-struck, on perceiving that he was headless!—but his horror was still more increased, on observing that the head, which should have rested on his shoulders, was carried before him on the pommel of the saddle: his terror rose to desperation; he rained a shower of kicks and blows upon Gunpowder, hoping, by a sudden movement, to give his companion the slip,—but the spectre started full jump with him. Away then they dashed, through thick and thin; stones flying, and sparks flashing at every bound. Ichabod's flimsy garments fluttered in the air, as he stretched his long lank body away over his horse's head, in the eagerness of his flight.

> Ichabod was horror-struck, on perceiving that he was headless!

They had now reached the road which turns off to Sleepy Hollow; but Gunpowder, who seemed possessed with a demon, instead of keeping up it, made an opposite turn, and plunged headlong downhill to the left. This road leads through a sandy hollow, shaded by trees for about a quarter of a mile, where it crosses the bridge famous in goblin story, and just beyond swells the green knoll on which stands the whitewashed church.

As yet the panic of the steed had given his unskillful rider an apparent advantage in the chase; but just as he had got halfway through the hollow, the girths of the saddle gave way, and he felt it slipping from under him. He seized it by the pommel, and endeavored to hold it firm, but in vain; and had just time to save himself by clasping old Gunpowder round the neck, when the saddle fell to the earth, and he heard it trampled underfoot by his pursuer. For a moment, the terror of Hans Van Ripper's wrath passed across his mind—for it was his Sunday saddle; but this was no time for petty fears; the goblin was hard on his haunches; and (unskillful rider that he was!) he had much ado to maintain his seat; sometimes slipping on one side, sometimes on another, and sometimes jolted on the high ridge of his horse's backbone, with a violence that he verily feared would cleave him asunder.

An opening in the trees now cheered him with the hopes that the church-bridge was at hand. The wavering reflection of a silver star in the bosom of the brook told him that he was not mistaken. He saw the wall of the church dimly glaring under the trees beyond. "If I can but reach that bridge," thought Ichabod, "I am safe." Just then he heard the black steed panting and blowing close behind him; he even fancied that he felt his hot breath. Another convulsive kick in the ribs, and old Gunpowder sprang upon the bridge; he thundered over the resounding planks; he gained the opposite side; and now Ichabod cast a look behind to see if his pursuer should vanish, according to rule, in a flash of fire and brimstone. Just then he saw the goblin rising in his stirrups, and in the very act of hurling his head at him. Ichabod endeavored to dodge the horrible missile, but too late. It encountered his cranium with a tremendous crash,—he was tumbled headlong into the dust, and Gunpowder, the black steed, and the goblin rider, passed by like a whirlwind.

"If I can but reach that bridge," thought Ichabod, "I am safe."

The next morning the old horse was found without his saddle, and with the bridle under his feet, soberly cropping the grass at his master's gate. Ichabod did not make his appearance at breakfast;—dinner-hour came, but no Ichabod. The boys assembled at the schoolhouse, and strolled idly about the banks of the brook; but no schoolmaster. Hans Van Ripper now began to feel some uneasiness about the fate of poor Ichabod, and his saddle. An inquiry was set on foot, and after diligent investigation they came upon his traces. In one part of the road leading to the church was found the saddle trampled in the dirt; the tracks of horses' hoofs deeply dented in the road, and evidently at furious speed, were traced to the bridge, beyond which, on the bank of a broad part of the brook, where the water ran deep and black, was found the hat of the unfortunate Ichabod, and close beside it a shattered pumpkin.

The brook was searched, but the body of the schoolmaster was not to be discovered.

Skeletons, Sorcerers and Spooks:
SPINE-TINGLING TRIVIA

1. What is a doppelganger?

2. What is the best way to bury vampires?

3. Who was the hydra, and who defeated it?

4. What is the name given to cloaked skeleton that personifies Death and carries a scythe and hourglass?

5. What are ghosts called in the tradition of voodoo?

6. Why do we commonly associate crows with death?

7. What type of sorcery involves conjuring the spirits of the dead in order to see into and influence the future?

8. How did pit vipers get their name, and where do they store their fangs when they are not striking their prey?

9. Which modern-day house pet was considered by some ancient civilizations to be the vilest of evil creatures?

10. What creature loves silver, but shrinks from silk and salt?

---

1. A "ghost" that is in the image of a person who is still living. The word comes from the German *doppel*, meaning "double," and *ganger*, meaning "goer." 2. Upside-down. That way, instead of prying its way out of a coffin, it was believed the vampire would dig his way straight into hell. 3. The hydra was a mythical monster with nine heads. Each time its foes tried to injure it by lopping off a head, two more would grow back in its place. Hercules destroyed the hydra as one of his famous twelve labors. 4. The Grim Reaper. 5. Zombies. 6. This association dates back to the Greeks, whose three similar sounding words, *chronus* (meaning "time"), *Cronus* (King of the Titans and Zeus's father), and *corone* (meaning "loose crow"), have come to be related. Cronus, the harvest god, carried a sickle and is the precursor to the Grim Reaper. 7. Necromancy. 8. Pit vipers—examples are rattlesnakes, fer-de-lances, copperheads, and water moccasins—have a heat-sensitive gland or "pit" at either side of their head that helps them detect when warm-blooded creatures are near. Their fangs retract and sit against the roof of their mouths when not in use. 9. The cat. 10. A ghost.

Hocus Pocus!

Sleight-of-hand performers, conjurers, and illusionists have been fooling people for centuries. But you don't have to be a Houdini to keep your friends guessing. A few simple tricks can get you on your way to a being a master magician!

Stacked Dice

Two dice, pencil, paper

1. Ask a volunteer to roll the dice while you have your back turned. Tell him or her to stack one die on top of the other.
2. Ask, "Got it?" and turn around to make sure the dice are stacked. Quickly note the number on top of the stack and subtract this number from fourteen. Say, "Good," and turn your back once again to the volunteer.
3. Keeping your back to the volunteer, write the result of your subtraction on a slip of paper, fold it, and place it on the table. Then tell your volunteer that there are three sides of the dice that cannot be seen: the one facing the table, and the two sides that are facing each other. Ask him or her to peek at each hidden side and add those three numbers together.
4. Ask the volunteer to tell you the total. Then have him or her unfold the paper you placed on the table. The numbers will be the same!

X Marks the Spot

*Two identical felt-tip pens,
old paperback book, paper*

1. To prepare, first leave the lid off one of the felt pens until it dries out. Then flip to the middle of the book and find a full page of text. Mark a big, sloppy *X* on the page with the working felt pen. Make sure the intersection of the lines clearly falls on a single word. Note that word.

2. When you are ready to perform the trick, announce that you will demonstrate your amazing extrasensory abilities. Ask for a volunteer to hold the book behind his or her back and flip it open to a page somewhere in the middle of the book. Hand your volunteer the pen that doesn't work and tell him or her to draw a large *X* on the open page while still holding the book behind his or her back.

3. Have the volunteer close the book. Then take a moment to "concentrate" on the word intersected by the *X*. Write that word on a piece of paper and hand it to the volunteer.

4. Ask your volunteer to find the page in the book marked with the X and tell you the word crossed by the X. They will find the X you made earlier with the working pen. Then have the volunteer read what you wrote on the paper. It's the same word!

Hocus Pocus!

Magic Fingers

Two nickels

1. Tell your friends you have magic fingers.
2. Lay one nickel heads up on the table and let each person try to balance the second nickel on it. It will be hard to do.
3. Wiggle your fingers and tell your friends to step aside. Then lay a nickel tails up on the table. Balance the edge of the second nickel across the two middle columns of the Monticello building. (Practice this before performing the trick.)

Magic Fingers II

One raw egg

1. Tell your friends you have magic fingers.
2. Let your friends try to balance the egg on its end on a table. It will be hard to do!
3. Wiggle your fingers and tell your friends to step aside. Take the egg and shake it hard in the air for a while. (You can close your eyes and mumble some magic words while you do this.) You need to shake the egg until the white and the yolk are mixed.
4. Balance the egg. (Practice this with another egg before performing the trick. Your chances of balancing an egg are good when the yolk is broken and settled on the bottom of the egg.)

Disappearing Penny

One penny, a glass of water, handkerchief

1. Out of your audience's sight, place a penny in the palm of a hand and a glass of water on top of it. The penny should look like it is IN the glass of water.
2. Tell your audience you can make a penny disappear. Show them the glass of water, then cover the glass with the handkerchief. Say the magic words.
3. Have a volunteer take the glass from your hand and remove the handkerchief. The penny will be gone. (The trick is to fold your hand quickly over the penny when your friend takes the glass.)

SCIENCE TRICKS

*S*cience can feel like magic much of the time. Put on a "magic" show for your friends with these great experiments! They will think you are a talented magician or a genius!

Magnetic Fields

iron filings, three magnets (round, bar, and u-shaped), three sheets of paper, paper cup

1. Place your iron filings in the paper cup.
2. Set the three magnets out on a table with a sheet of paper covering each.
3. Sprinkle each paper with iron filings and watch them quickly form patterns on the paper.

PRINCIPLES AT WORK: The iron filings are pulled into the magnetic field of the respective magnets. The closer the filings are to the magnet, the more force is exerted on them. For the bar and *u*-shaped magnets, the force is strongest at the ends, so more filings should gather there. The force is equal around all the edges of the round magnet, so the filings will create a circular pattern.

Pendulum

tennis ball, string (approximately 6 feet long), thumbtack

1. Tie one end of your string tightly around the tennis ball. Attach the other end to the ceiling (at least 4 feet from the nearest wall) with the thumbtack. You may alternately tie the other end to a tree branch.
2. Ask your friend to hold the tennis ball so that it is just touching the tip of his or her nose and walk backward until the the string is taut.
3. Release the ball to begin the pendulum motion.

4. The ball will swing out and back but it will not touch your friend. It'll just make him flinch!

PRINCIPLES AT WORK: Pendulums work on the principle of periodic motion. This means that theoretically, the ball should continue to swing out and back, forever, touching the tip of your friends nose each time. However, gravity, the friction of the string and its attach point, and the air resistance against the ball and string cause the pendulum to slow with each swing until it eventually stops.

Surface Tension
strainer, cooking oil, shallow bowl, small glass of water

1. Coat the wire mesh of your strainer with cooking oil either by pouring it through the strainer into the bowl or dipping the strainer into a small bowl of oil.
2. Holding the coated strainer over the sink, carefully add the glass of water. The water should stay inside of the strainer.
3. Ask your friend to touch the underside of the strainer with their fingers or a toothpick. The water should run out of the strainer into the sink.

PRINCIPLES AT WORK: The water stays inside the strainer at first because the oil coats the rough wire and creates a "skin" of surface tension. The molecules of water already have a very strong attraction, and the oil helps reinforce the attraction to fight against gravity and the sharp edges of the wire mesh. The surface tension bonds are broken once your friend's hand or toothpick breaks the surface of the oil.

Supervillians!

They are the ones you know and love. From the all-powerful might of the cosmos-roaming Galactus to the world-domineering ambitions of Dr. Doom, they come in all shapes and sizes, and sometimes even with an extra pair of arms or two, because who couldn't use a spare pair of hands to create chaos?

THE ABOMINATION

The Abomination originates as a spy named Emil Blonsky who manages to penetrate the Air Force base that houses Dr. Bruce Banner's gamma-ray research. Blonsky stumbles upon Banner's gamma-ray machine, exposing himself to the ray's effects. The gamma radiation is so strong and concentrated (more than the radiation that transforms the Hulk) it changes him into a monster. He is now doomed to walk the earth as a hateful, scaly, superhuman creature. The Abomination's incredible strength and stamina rivals that of his greatest nemesis, the Hulk. Unlike the Hulk, the Abomination retains his intellect.

DR. DOOM

As a college classmate of Reed Richards (later Mr. Fantastic), Victor Von Doom is an equally brilliant but arrogant scientist who becomes hideously disfigured by an explosion. Masked by a metal faceplate and impenetrable body armor, Dr. Doom takes control of his homeland, the small European country of Latveria. Not content with one nation, his ultimate aspiration is world domination. In his armor, which incorporates a force field and concussion beams, Dr. Doom can lift about 2 tons. The ability to switch minds with others is his only superpower, which he seldom uses; he more than makes up for this, however, with his enormous arsenal of cutting-edge weaponry.

DR. OCTOPUS

Brilliant atomic scientist Otto Octavius invents a tool to help him in his lab—four robotic tentacles, with claws, that are as fast as whips, strong as jackhammers, and made of steel. His colleagues dub him "Dr. Octopus" when he wears them attached to his torso. But when a freak accident fuses the tentacles to his body and gives him telepathic control over them, Dr. Octopus forgets all about scientific research and devotes his life to riches, crime, and the defeat of his enemy, Spiderman.

GALACTUS

Before there is Galactus, there is Galan, a citizen of the planet Taa. When this race of knowledge-seeking beings is destroyed by radiation, only Galan survives. The almighty power of the universe reaches out to him and transforms him into Galactus, a being with godlike, unlimited powers and the ability to channel all the energy in the universe for his use. Unfortunately, Galactus must travel through the cosmos devouring entire civilizations in order to survive.

Supervillians!

GREEN GOBLIN

An accident involving an untested, experimental formula grants Norman Osborn—ruthless co-owner of a leading chemical-manufacturing enterprise—superhuman strength, a heightened intellect, and an accelerated healing factor. Outfitting himself with Pumpkin Bombs and a gravity-defying Goblin-Glider, Osborn, a.k.a. the Green Goblin, embarks on a crime spree. He becomes fixated with killing the wise-cracking, wall-crawling superhero known as "Spiderman" thinking he will then attain instant credibility among the citizens of the underworld. After he discovers the hero's true identity—college student Peter Parker, who also is Osborn's son Harry's best friend—Green Goblin uses this information to terrorize Peter Parker's friends and loved ones. He is Spiderman's greatest enemy.

Green Goblin's arsenal includes incendiary grenades cast in the form of miniature jack-o'-lanterns; smoke- and gas-emitting bombs; a high-flying Goblin Glider, and gloves capable of discharging electrical pulses of up to 10,000 volts. The Green Goblin also develops a gas that can neutralize Spiderman's early-warning danger sense for a limited period.

THE JOKER

Little is known about the man who becomes the Joker. A failed stand-up comedian learns of his wife's death in a freakish accident and gets involved in a robbery at the chemical corporation where he works. When confronted by Batman, he dives into a river of chemical waste and emerges a different man—his skin is chalk white, his lips a shocking red, and his hair a monstrous green. The sight of it drives him mad, and soon Gotham City's most prominent citizens are laughing themselves to death, with a permanent smile. Batman's most diabolical nemesis emerges.

Supervillians!

LEX LUTHOR

Lex Luthor, warped to the core, is Superman's lifelong nemesis. The source of Luthor's enmity begins in Smallville when they are teenagers. Says Superman, "My arch-enemy, Luthor, might have been the world's greatest benefactor! But he lost his hair in an accidental explosion and blamed me for his baldness! In his bitterness he became Earth's most evil criminal scientist!"

As evil as he is brilliant, Luthor carries out his villainous plots from any number of secret hideouts. Superman foils plot after plot, earning Luthor's undying hatred.

The Road Not Taken

by Robert Frost

Two roads diverged in a yellow wood,
And sorry I could not travel both
And be one traveler, long I stood
And looked down one as far as I could
To where it bent in the undergrowth;

Then took the other, as just as fair,
And having perhaps the better claim,
Because it was grassy and wanted wear;
Though as for that, the passing there
Had worn them really about the same,

And both that morning equally lay
In leaves no step had trodden black.
Oh, I kept the first for another day!
Yet knowing how way leads on to way,
I doubted if I should ever come back.

I shall be telling this with a sigh
Somewhere ages and ages hence:
Two roads diverged in a wood, and I—
I took the one less traveled by,
And that has made all the difference.

YOUGEST RELAY TEAM TO SWIM THE CHANNEL

The youngest six-member relay team to cross the English Channel was the Thane District AAA team from Mumbai (Bombay), India, who swam from Shakespeare Beach, Dover, Kent, UK, to Cap Gris-Nez, France, in 11 hrs. 23 mins. on Aug. 12, 1996. The team members were Kaveri Thakur (13), Rahul Modi (13), Daniel Reuben (13), Gunjan Parulkar (14), Rashmi Sansare (14), and Siddesh Parab (14).

YOUNGEST CHAMPION

The youngest successful competitor in a world title event was a French boy, whose name is not recorded, who coxed the Netherlands' Olympic pair in the rowing competition at Paris, France, on Aug. 26 1900. He was not more than 10 and may have been as young as 7.

Young Champions

YOUNGEST PLAYER TO SCORE A HAT TRICK The youngest scorer of a hat trick (3 goals in a game) in UK football was Tommy Lawton, age 17 years, 5 days, for Burnley v. Spurs at Turf Moor on Oct. 10, 1936. The youngest player to score a hat trick in the Premiership was Michael Owen, (UK), age 18 years, 62 days, for Liverpool v. Sheffield on Wednesday, Feb. 14, 1998.

YOUNGEST ATHLETICS WORLD-RECORD HOLDER The youngest male to set an official world record is Thomas Ray (UK), who was 17 years, 198 days when he set a pole-vault record of 11 ft 2.75 in (3.42m) on Sept. 19, 1879.

YOUNGEST CONCRETE BLOCK BREAKER David Chu Tan (Germany), trained by his father—a martial arts master—was 11 years old when he managed to break 24 concrete blocks with his head in 30 seconds while doing a forward back flip—one for every two blocks. He set this record on Dec. 20, 2000. David's father had been training David since he was a small child.

DODGE BALL

Gotcha!

Number of players: at least twelve
(an even number per team)

What you need: a large rubber ball,
a large open area to run in

Split the group into two teams. Each team stays on their side of a dividing line. The game begins when one player throws the ball across the dividing line at one of the opposing players. If the player is hit, then that player is out of the game. If the player catches the ball, then the player who threw the ball is out of the game. If no one is hit, then the other team gets a chance to throw the ball. If any player on either team touches or crosses the dividing line, they are out of the game. The game ends when every member of one of the teams is out.

Note: Since it's possible to throw the rubber ball pretty hard, it's a good idea to have a parent watch over the game to make sure it doesn't get too rough.

Fun&Games

RED ROVER

Hold on tight!

Number of players: at least eight
(an even number per team)

What you need: a large open area to run in

Split the group into two teams. Each team lines up shoulder to shoulder, holding hands. The teams face each other about ten to twenty feet apart. A coin toss decides which team goes first. The game begins when one player calls on one of the opposing players by reciting, "Red Rover, Red Rover, send [name of player] over!" The player who is called separates from his/her team, picks out a weak link in the human chain and charges, trying to break through the joined hands of the opposite side. If the player succeeds, he/she gets to take one of the players from the other side over to join his/her team. If the payer fails, then he/she becomes a member of the opposite team. The game ends when one team is out of players.

RACES

HOPPING   All of the players must hop from a starting line to a finish line. Whoever crosses the finish line first wins.

WALKING   All of the players must walk (not run) from starting line to finish line. Whoever crosses the finish line first wins. To make things interesting, have each of the players carry an egg on a spoon, a bean on a butter knife, an item on their head, etc. If a player drops the item they're carrying, they have to start over from the starting line.

WHEELBARROW   Break the players up into pairs. One player walks on his/her hands while the other player holds him/her by the feet or legs, guiding the "human wheelbarrow" to the finish line. The first pair across the finish line wins.

POTATO-SACK RACE   Each player steps into a sack that reaches up to his/her midsection. Players hold on to their sacks with their hands and hop from a starting line to a finish line. Whoever crosses the finish line first wins.

Watch

Have you ever wondered how your watch keeps time? If you have a mechanical watch that requires winding from time to time, it is powered by what is called a mainspring.

As the spring unwinds, the two hands on your watch face move around the dial.

But how does that happen? It's all in the spur…gears—gears with teeth, that is. The unwinding mainspring turns a spur gear mechanism called a drive wheel. The drive wheel, with the aid of a minute wheel spur gear, "drives" the minute hand. The hour hand is driven by the two spur gears that are connected to the minute wheel. Together, these gears reduce the hour hand's speed to one-twelfth that of the minute hand.

But how does the drive wheel know how fast to go? The speed of the drive wheel is controlled by a mechanism called a lever escapement. A second spring, called a hairspring, swings to and fro, causing a lever in your watch to rock back and forth. The lever has pallets that hook into the teeth of the escape wheel gear. The pallets release the wheel, one tooth at a time. Then, a set of gears connects this all back up to the drive wheel. Whew! That's it!

Refrigerator

Can you imagine living in a world where cold milk, ice cream, and fresh meat were luxuries? Well that has been the way of the world throughout most of history. A reliable refrigerator was not introduced into homes until 1911.

The concept of modern refrigeration involves removing heat from an enclosed space using the process of evaporation. Have you ever rubbed alcohol on your skin? It's cold, isn't it? That's because as the alcohol evaporates, it absorbs the heat of your skin. Well, refrigerators work on a similar idea, only they use a liquid with an evaporation temperature that is much lower—it's called a refrigerant. (Never attempt to test how refrigerant would feel on your skin! It would freeze it instantly!) A *compressor*, the motor you hear inside the refrigerator, pumps the refrigerant, in vapor form, into heat-exchanging pipes called *coils*. High pressure forces the vapor back into a liquid. In the process, the vapor gives off heat, cooling the interior of the fridge. As the coils are at the back of the refrigerator, the heat is released into the air around the refrigerator. Next, the liquid passes through an *expansion valve* at low pressure. The low pressure causes the liquid to evaporate and become cold vapor again. The refrigerant runs back into the compressor, to start the process all over.

Homemade frozen treats can rival anything an ice-cream truck has to offer. Frozen pops made out of ice cream, yogurt, gelatin, fruit or juice are delicious and fun. Leftover small yogurt or sour-cream containers make ideal molds for your pops. Experiment with different ingredients to make the perfect frozen treat. You can simply freeze fruit dipped in chocolate, nuts, or honey. It can also be as easy as orange juice in ice trays. Happy freezing!

RASPBERRY TIE-DYE POPS

3 pints fresh or frozen raspberries
2 tablespoons freshly squeezed lemon juice
1 quart vanilla ice cream or frozen yogurt,
  softened
Popsicle molds
12 Popsicle sticks

1. In a blender, mix 2 1/2 pints of raspberries for about 1 minute, until nearly liquid. Pass puree through a very fine sieve to remove seeds and transfer mixture to a medium-size bowl.
2. Add 1 tablespoon lemon juice to pureed raspberries and mix well.
3. In blender, combine ice cream or yogurt with 1 tablespoon lemon juice until smooth.

4. Add layers of ice cream, fruit puree, and remaining raspberries to each pop mold. Insert a knife into mold and swirl several times to create a pattern.
5. Freeze for 15 minutes and then insert Popsicle stick halfway into each pop. Freeze overnight.

Makes 12 pops.

CHERRY MARSHMALLOW POPS

1 3-ounce package cherry-flavored gelatin
2 cups boiling water
7 ounces marshmallow creme
2 cups apple juice
10 6-ounce paper cups
$1^1/2$ cups mini-marshmallows
10 Popsicle sticks

1. In large bowl, stir gelatin into boiling water until dissolved.
2. Gradually add marshmallow creme and beat with hand mixer until well blended. Stir in juice.
3. Pour into paper cups. Press mini-marshmallows into gelatin with a chopstick or the end of a wooden spoon.
4. Cover each cup with aluminum foil. Carefully poke Popsicle sticks through foil and all the way into gelatin. Freeze overnight.
5. When you're ready for a pop, run hot water over the paper cups for 10 to 15 seconds to make it easy to remove the cup.

Makes 10 pops.

BANANA YOGURT POPS

2 bananas
2 ounces plain yogurt
$1/4$ cup milk
1 teaspoon sugar
6 4-ounce paper cups
6 Popsicle sticks

1. In a medium-size bowl, mash bananas with fork. Mix in yogurt, milk, and sugar until thoroughly blended.
2. Pour mixture into paper cups. Cover each cup with aluminum foil and carefully insert Popsicle sticks through foil and into mixture. Freeze overnight.

Makes 6 pops.

FROZEN PINEAPPLE POPS

10 strawberries, with stems removed
1 can (14 ounces) pineapple rings
6 ounces chocolate chips
bamboo skewers

1. Line a cookie sheet with wax paper and set aside.
2. Place one strawberry in the center of each pineapple ring.
3. With a bamboo skewer, carefully spear the pineapple from one side to the other through the middle of the strawberry.
4. Place skewered fruit on cookie sheet and freeze for one hour.
5. In microwavable bowl, melt chocolate on high for 2 to 3 minutes. Dip the top half of the frozen fruit sticks in the melted chocolate. Freeze for another hour, until the chocolate has hardened.

Makes 10 pops.

FROZEN BANANA ROCKETS

2 bananas
4 tablespoons honey
5 tablespoons chopped nuts
4 Popsicle sticks
baking sheet

1. Cut both bananas in half horizontally to make 4 chunky banana pieces.
2. Insert a Popsicle stick into the wide end of each banana piece.
3. Coat each piece in honey and roll in chopped nuts. Press the nuts into each banana piece so they will hold.
4. Place on baking sheet and freeze for about 2 hours, or until firm.

Makes 4 pops

SNOW CONES

2 cups orange juice
ice cube tray

1. Pour juice into ice cube tray and freeze overnight.
2. Put ice cubes in a blender. Turn blender on and off until ice is the consistency of snow. Serve immediately.

Serves 2.

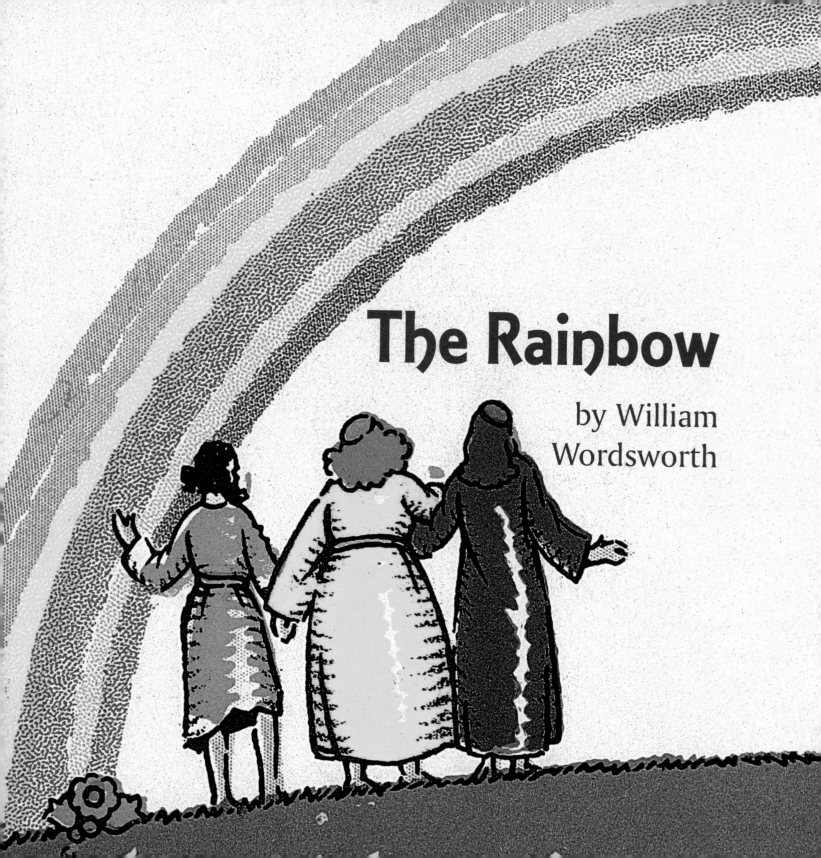

The Rainbow

by William
Wordsworth

My heart leaps up when I behold
　　A Rainbow in the sky:
So was it when my life began;
So is it now I am a Man;
So be it when I shall grow old,
　　Or let me die!
The Child is Father of the Man;
And I could wish my days to be
Bound each to each by natural piety.

Stop Time

Have you ever wanted to travel in time? Suppose you had the chance to meet people who live in the future and tell them something about yourself and life in the twenty-first century. Well, even if you can't build a time machine, you can bury one! Collect items that will capture a moment in time and seal them in a time capsule that won't be opened for 10, 50, or 5,000 years.

Large, airtight, waterproof, rustproof container, such as a glass jar or stainless steel box, resealable plastic bags, duct tape, label

1. Make your time-capsule list (see suggestions on right.)
2. Once you've gathered the ingredients of your time capsule, seal them in your airtight container. Make sure that none of the time capsule contents will rust or decay. For example, paper clips and staples will rust and can damage paper items over a long period of time. For extra protection against the elements, place paper items in resealable plastic bags.
3. Reinforce the seal on your time capsule with duct tape and add a label.
4. Decide how to store your time capsule. If you bury it, be sure to make a detailed map that will let future time-capsule seekers know where to dig! Or you could make arrangements to store your time capsule in a safe deposit box at a bank. Sit back, relax, and wait for the future to discover it!

Time Capsule Checklist

THINK ABOUT ITEMS THAT...

❏ HIGHLIGHT EVERYDAY EXPERIENCES:
toothbrush, article of clothing, pen, comb,
chewing gum, coins, food wrappers

❏ DEPICT POPULAR CULTURE:
comic book, music CD, videotape or
DVD, magazine, baseball, concert tickets, television guide

❏ REFLECT TRADITIONS AND CUSTOMS:
school yearbook, holiday cards and
decorations, calendar that notes
religious and national holidays, literature or poetry

❏ SHOW OFF THE LATEST TECHNOLOGY:
newspaper articles, advertisements,
printouts of Internet sites, photographs

❏ TELL SOMETHING ABOUT YOURSELF:
a letter from you that includes information about yourself and your everyday
life, your hopes and dreams, and predic-
tions of the future (you might also
enclose artwork, personal memorabilia,
jewelry, a favorite toy or game)

GAMES for the ROAD

You've probably asked "How long till we get there?" more than once on a road trip. The next time you visit relatives or go on vacation, you can beat backseat boredom with a handful of games that don't require much more than your imagination. Now, getting there can be half the fun!

ALPHABET GAME

Players look for words that begin with each letter of the alphabet on road signs, billboards, buildings, train cars, or semi trucks. (License plate letters don't count.) When you find your A word, you must call it out so that no one else can claim it. Then you can go on to B, and so forth. (You can't call words out of order!) The tough letters are usually Q, X, and Z. So be sure to look for a Quick Mart after the RR Xing where there's a Speed Zone Ahead.

BOTTICELLI

One player thinks of a famous person or character. Everyone else takes turns asking yes or no questions. The player who guesses correctly wins the round and gets to lead the next one.

GOING ON A PICNIC

The first player recites the phrase, "I'm going on a picnic and I'm bringing _____." He or she fills in the blank with a word beginning with the letter A, such as APPLES. The second person recites the phrase and adds a B word: "I'm going on a picnic and I'm bringing APPLES and BANANAS." Each additional turn requires reciting the whole phrase and adding a new word that begins with the next letter of the alphabet. Whoever can't recite the growing list of items in proper order loses.

GEOGRAPHY

Players choose a category, such as cities, countries, rivers, or landmarks. The first player names something from that category. The next player must think of another name that starts with the last letter of the first name. For example, a city list could start: San Francisco, Omaha, Akron, New York, Kansas City. If a player can't think of another city, that person is out. The last player in the game wins.

GHOST

The first player says a letter. The next player must think of a word that starts with that letter and give a second letter. The object is for each player to add a letter without ending the word. (Two- and three-letter words don't count.) For example, the letter called out is B. The next player adds U, thinking of BUSY. The third player adds M, thinking of BUMP. If the next player adds a P, he would lose the round. A smart choice would be the letter B (for bumble), to continue the round. The first player to end the word gets a letter G. A person who gets all the letters to spell GHOST loses.

Tongue Twisters

Peter Piper picked a peck of pickled peppers
A peck of pickled peppers Peter Piper picked
If Peter Piper picked a peck of pickled peppers
Where's the peck of pickled peppers Peter Piper picked?

A flea and a fly flew up in a flue.
Said the flea, "Let us fly!"
Said the fly, "Let us flee!"
So they flew through a flaw in the flue!

A Tudor who tooted a flute
tried to tutor two tooters to toot.
Said the two to their tutor,
"Is it harder to toot
or to tutor two tooters to toot?"

I saw Esau kissing Kate,
And Kate saw I saw Esau,
And Esau saw that I saw Kate,
And Kate saw I saw Esau saw.

Oliver Oglethorp ogled
an owl and an oyster.

Did Oliver
Oglethorp ogle
an owl and
an oyster?

If Oliver
Oglethorp ogled an
owl and an oyster,

Where are the
owl and the
oyster Oliver
Oglethorp
ogled?

Cheerily, then, my little man,
Live and laugh,
As boyhood can!

—John Grenleaf Whitier